'You have bewitched

Sandi wante ...   ... er
remark that v ...   ... y,
but her mou ...   ... s
pounding like ...

'I don't like th ...   ... other men have
touched you, k ... you,' Jacques continued
huskily. 'You know that?'

He meant Ian, and suddenly the name was a
talisman to hold off this feeling that was utterly
new to her, this fierce, deep, primitive desire
that had a vibrant sexual awareness at its base,
and something else—something she didn't
recognise. 'You mean my husband?' she asked
flatly.

'Your dead husband,' he corrected softly, his
face hardening. 'He's dead, Sandi. Dead.
Whatever you shared, it is over.'

'I know that.' She swung away from him.

'No, I do not think you do...'

Helen Brooks lives in Northamptonshire and is married with three children. As she is a committed Christian, busy housewife and mother, her spare time is at a premium but her hobbies include reading, swimming, gardening and walking her two energetic, inquisitive and very endearing young dogs. Her long-cherished aspiration to write became a reality when she put pen to paper on reaching the age of forty, and sent the result off to Mills & Boon.

Recent titles by the same author:

THE MARRIAGE SOLUTION
DREAM WEDDING

RECKLESS FLIRTATION

BY
HELEN BROOKS

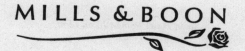

MILLS & BOON

All the characters in this book have no existence outside the imagination of the author, and have no relation whatsoever to anyone bearing the same name or names. They are not even distantly inspired by any individual known or unknown to the author, and all the incidents are pure invention.

MILLS & BOON and the Rose Device
are trademarks of the publisher.
Harlequin Mills & Boon Limited,
Eton House, 18-24 Paradise Road, Richmond, Surrey TW9 1SR

ISBN 0 263 79737 6

Set in Times Roman 10 on 11 pt.
01-9610-62310 C1

Made and printed in Great Britain

CHAPTER ONE

'MRS CHALLIER? How do you do?' The cool, deep voice was as distant as the dark, handsome face staring down at her. 'You are Mrs Ann Challier?' The attractive French accent, so like Emile's, was chilling.

'I—' Sandi hesitated for a split second, her mind racing.

'I was informed this was the residence of Mrs Ann Challier.' The aristocratic face was as cold as ice, and the fine aquiline nose almost wrinkled with distaste as he spoke the word 'residence'. 'This is not so?'

'Who are you?' Sandi ignored the niceties of social intercourse as the fine hairs on the back of her neck stiffened warningly. This was one of them, she just knew it. But which one?

'I think you know who I am.' The hard face didn't give an inch. 'Emile must have mentioned me, surely?'

Sandi stared at the tall, broad-shouldered stranger as she searched her mind quickly. It had to be either André or Jacques. The likeness to Emile was too strong for there not to be a blood tie, but which brother was it? Whichever one, that lean, muscled body and hard, ruthless face spelt trouble with a capital T—and no way was this man coming within three feet of her sister. 'I'm not in the mood to play games, Mr—?'

'Games?' For a moment she almost closed the door in his face as the dark eyes glittered menacingly. 'I do not play games, Mrs Challier. I am Emile's brother Jacques. I regret the imposition at such a delicate time, but I trust you understand we need to talk—'

5

'You have got to be joking!' So this was the great and venerable Jacques Challier, was it? She might have known. The flood of pure undiluted rage that swept through her slight form brought her chin jerking upwards and her eyes flashing blue sparks as she surveyed the immaculately dressed man in the doorway. 'I wouldn't talk to one of your despicable clan if you were the last family left alive on earth, Mr Challier,' she said tightly. 'And for the record I'm not Ann, I'm her sister, Sandi. But you can take it as read that I'm voicing my sister's thoughts as well as my own.'

'I beg your pardon—' The frosty, icy voice was cut off in mid-stream.

'No, you don't!' She was almost crouched in the doorway now as she spat her rage and anger and bitter hurt at him. 'The illustrious Challier family have never begged in their life. Force is more in your line, isn't it? That and nasty not so subtle manoeuvring of people's lives and happiness. Well, you should all be happy now, back in your wonderful, precious château, shouldn't you? Emile is dead and you've broken Ann's heart— what more do you want?'

'You dare to talk to me like this?' The French accent was very pronounced and his face was as white as a sheet, but nothing could have stopped her from speaking her mind to this unfeeling block of stone.

'Oh, yes, I dare, Mr Challier. I most certainly dare,' she hissed hotly, straightening sharply as he made to push past her into the tiny flat and barring the way with her small body like an enraged tigress defending her young. 'No further!' Her voice, quiet as it now was, stopped him in his tracks as he recognised the throbbing hate in its depths.

'You're not coming into this flat. I'd rather die than let you soil Ann's home with your filthy presence,' she said softly. 'You can leave her alone now; the only thing that linked her with your family has gone. We're not intimidated by your wealth or influence, Mr Challier, not any more. My sister wasn't good enough for your precious family, was she? She didn't have the right connections and she wasn't French.' Her lips had drawn back from her teeth as though she was looking at something repugnant, and the tall man standing in front of her was as still as a statue.

'Well, let me tell you something—something you can take back home with you for the rest of them. She's worth more than all the Challiers put together. In fact, you aren't worthy to lick her boots, any of you. Emile knew that. At least they had a few months of happiness together, and none of you can take that away. If you're worried we'll make any claims on the Challier fortune, you can forget it. We despise and detest you all. There is nothing—*nothing*—we want from you. Have I made myself clear?'

'Transparently so.' The black eyes were narrowed slits, but otherwise the hard face was expressionless. 'I could even say dramatically so.'

'You can say whatever you like,' Sandi answered softly. 'You can't hurt Emile any more and I won't let you hurt Ann.'

She saw the import of her words register in his eyes at the same moment as a faint female voice reached out through the door separating them. 'Sandi? Sandi, who's there?'

'It's all right, Ann. I'll be with you in a minute.' She turned back to him and her hand moved to close the door. 'Goodbye, Mr Challier.'

'And this is your final word?' He stiffened as her intention to send him on his way unheard hit home.

'You'd better believe it,' she said tightly, a small part of her mind acknowledging that this was probably the first time in his life that he had been actively thwarted— and by a female at that. Ann had told her that Emile had often joked that Jacques, as the older brother and partner in their father's huge and successful wine business, had more women than he knew what to do with. Having seen him, she could believe it.

'The conversation would have been to your sister's financial benefit—'

'What is it with you people?' she asked with horrified contempt, not bothering to control her scorn. 'Is money your god? Is that it? Well, rest assured it isn't ours. Ann has her memories and—' She stopped abruptly and bit her lip as she realised what she had been about to say. 'And that's enough,' she finished carefully. 'So you've fulfilled your obligation to your brother's widow, Mr Challier. You've made the gesture of a blood-offering to appease your guilt, and now I would like you to leave. My sister hasn't been able to sleep for days. This is the first time she's rested during the day and now you've woken her up—'

'Oh, come, Miss—?' Sandi ignored the request for her name with a raising of her chin and a narrowing of her eyes as she stared back into the dark face looking down at her so contemptuously, and after waiting a few seconds he shrugged coldly. 'This is the age of sleeping pills and other such medication for difficult circumstances. I'm sure her doctor has prescribed—'

'She can't have sleeping pills—' Again she stopped suddenly and took a deep breath, furious with herself for being provoked into responding to his scornful cynicism without thinking about what she was going to say first. 'Look, just go away, will you?' she hissed tightly as her voice returned along with her wits. 'We don't want you here.'

As she made to slam the door a large male foot moved quickly into the opening. At the same moment his body took the force of her action, his shoulder effectively checking the door's momentum. 'Not so fast, Ann's sister,' he said softly, his voice like liquid steel. 'There is something here I do not understand—'

'There's nothing *to* understand,' she spat back quietly, her voice shaking. 'I don't want you upsetting Ann, that's all. Just leave us alone—'

As the door to one side of the small hall opened her voice stopped abruptly, and both their faces turned to the young girl standing swaying in the doorway. And even though her thin, slender body emphasised her swollen stomach, heavy with child, a young and vulnerable girl was still exactly what Ann Challier looked like. A beautiful, pale, lost child, with long, tangled strawberry-blonde hair and haunted dazed eyes the colour of a summer sky that widened on fastening on the tall, silent man in the doorway.

'No...' The bewildered, frightened gaze moved fleetingly to Sandi. 'Sandi? No...'

And as she slipped helplessly into a dead faint they both moved as one—Jacques reaching Ann just a second before Sandi and catching her body before it hit the floor. He sank to his knees with her in his arms.

'Look what you've done.' Sandi, too, had crouched down over her sister's inert body, and now they faced each other across Ann's unconscious form. 'Oh, why did you have to come here today? You didn't even bother to acknowledge the funeral—why come here now and upset her like this?'

'She's having a child.' The heavily accented voice was as stunned as the dark face. 'Is it Emile's?'

'*Of course it's Emile's.*' Sandi glared at him so savagely that he blinked. 'Who on earth did you think—? Oh, you Challiers!'

'I didn't mean it like that.' He shook his head slightly. 'But I didn't know. We were not informed—'

'Why should you have been informed?' she asked tightly. 'You and your family made it perfectly clear that if Emile married my sister he was, to all intents and purposes, dead in your eyes. Well, now he is, isn't he?' Her face was as white as his, but her eyes were scorching with the force of her emotion.

'The poor boy was working all hours—doing his degree by day and a job at night, catching a few hours' sleep whenever he could. But you don't care, not really. You've never cared. What do your type, with all your millions, know about hard work anyway?' she asked scathingly. 'He was killed while driving back to his depot, if you're interested. The police think he fell asleep at the wheel of the van, because there was no reason for it to plough into the brick wall he hit.'

'I have read the police report,' he said stiffly.

'But you couldn't make the funeral?' she asked slowly. 'But why should you, after all? He was only your brother, the black sheep who had stepped outside of the Challier regime and was therefore less than nothing.'

'I came as soon as I found out,' he said sharply, his eyes glittering as they met hers. 'We were away. My mother has not been well and needed a complete rest away from all outside contact.'

'And this "complete rest" was without telephones?' she asked disbelievingly. 'The police must have tried to contact you—'

'They did, and eventually they succeeded,' he said coldly. 'As you see.'

'What I see—' The harsh retort she had been about to make was cut off as Ann moaned softly and her eyelids flickered and moved.

'Could you carry her to the bedroom?' Sandi asked quickly, hating the necessity but knowing that she couldn't leave Ann lying on the threadbare carpet in the small hall. 'She's been ill ever since it happened. Since Emile's accident,' she added quietly but with a wealth of bitterness in her voice.

'Of course. If you will permit me?' He moved a hand under Ann's limp body and lifted her into his arms as though she weighed less than nothing, and as he rose

Sandi led the way into the flat's minute box of a bedroom, drawing back the quilt and covering her sister's limp body as soon as Jacques had laid her on the bed.

As she did so, Ann's lovely eyes opened slowly, her fist going immediately to her mouth as her gaze centred on Jacques's dark face, which was an older version of Emile's.

'It's all right, Ann, it's all right.' Sandi crouched over her sister, blocking her from her brother-in-law's gaze. 'You've fainted, that's all.'

'Who—?'

'It's Jacques,' Sandi said quietly. 'But it's all right, I promise. He just wanted...' She hesitated and forced herself to go on in a neutral, steady voice. 'He just wanted to see if there was anything he could do to help.'

'Help?' There was a touch of hysteria in her sister's voice that the tall man standing so silently just behind them heard and recognised.

'Mrs Challier?' To Sandi's fury he moved round to the other side of the bed, drawing Ann's gaze to him as he looked down at her, his face amazingly gentle and quiet. 'I wish you no harm, please believe me.' Sandi saw her sister flinch as her exhausted gaze took in the remarkable likeness to her dead husband, but Jacques had continued speaking before she had time to react. 'We had no idea of Emile's accident until just a few hours ago,' he said quietly. 'It is important that you understand this. My mother is unfortunately not well herself, and the news—naturally so—proved a great blow to her—'

'Look, what exactly do you want?' As Sandi spoke again the dark eyes turned to her, and she was immediately conscious of her faded T-shirt, old, worn blue jeans and the fact that her face was devoid of make-up. The deep brown eyes that had been so quiet and intent as they'd looked at Ann now hardened into glinting onyx as they fastened on her face.

He, on the other hand, was dressed with the unmistakable elegance of limitless wealth. His clothes—casual, but screaming an exclusive designer label that put them in the unattainable bracket—sat on the big male frame in a way guaranteed to make most red-blooded females take a second look.

'My sister is very tired, and the funeral yesterday was the worst sort of ordeal in her condition.'

'Of course—'

'She needs rest and quiet, and I have to say that your presence is not conducive to either,' Sandi continued quickly, before she lost her nerve. There was something very intimidating about Jacques Challier—a fact she felt that he was well aware of and used to good advantage—but she was blowed if she was going to be terrorised by him or any other member of the family who had treated her sister so cruelly.

She saw dark red colour flare briefly under the high classical cheekbones, but other than that there was no trace that her words had hit home; his whole stance was one of cold contempt and autocratic imperiousness as he faced her over the bed. 'This attitude is not helping any of us,' he said coolly. 'Your sister least of all.'

'I think you can safely leave my sister's welfare to me,' she answered just as coldly, and her heart thudded so hard that she felt he would hear it.

'I'm sure she is in most capable hands.' His eyes had narrowed to black slits, his gaze sweeping again over her slight figure and the mass of corn-coloured hair tied high on the top of her head in a voluptuous ponytail of silky gold curls.

'Yes, she is.' Sandi's gaze didn't waver, even though she knew he was speaking tongue-in-cheek. 'So, if you don't mind...?' She waved her hand towards the door in a gesture of dismissal.

'Not at all.' He turned quietly to Ann, nodding his head in a formal little bow that was pure French. 'There are one or two formalities, you understand, but as it seems your sister is dealing with such things I will talk to her, yes?'

It wasn't quite what Sandi had had in mind, but as long as he left Ann alone she didn't much care, she thought shakily as she noticed her sister's strained white face and tense eyes. At this rate she would lose the baby, and if that happened—

'Yes...' Ann's voice was a mere whisper, but it seemed to satisfy him because he turned in the next instant, leaving the room after another nod at them both and shutting the door carefully behind him.

'I'll go and see what he wants.' Sandi forced a smile as she spoke, patting her sister's hand reassuringly. 'It won't take long.'

'I'm sorry, Sandi.' Ann had half raised herself in the bed when the door closed, and now her eyes were bright with unshed tears. 'But he looked so much like Emile that for a minute I thought... Oh, I shouldn't involve you like this.'

'Don't be silly.' Sandi plumped down on the bed, taking her sister's too thin body in her arms and giving her a quick hug before standing again. She was too slender, she thought worriedly. Even before Emile's accident the pregnancy had been a difficult one, and although the doctors were satisfied that the baby was getting all it needed it was clear that Ann was suffering in consequence. 'If you can't involve me, who can you, for goodness' sake? I told you yesterday—I'm staying as long as you need me here and I mean it.'

'But your job—?'

'No job is as important as you,' Sandi said firmly. 'If they won't keep it open for me until I get back that's their loss, not mine.' Brave words, but her stomach lurched at the thought of what she might be throwing away.

She had had to leave university eight years ago, halfway through her degree, to look after Ann when their parents had died. She had known that a career would be that much more difficult without the necessary qualifications, but she had done it gladly, knowing that her sensitive, delicate sister would have wilted and pined with strangers.

After getting a foothold on the ladder of advertising she had proved herself both gifted and tenacious, and when her chance had come eight months ago she had reached out and grasped it. And the job, based in America, was a dream. Her own flat, car, and a monthly salary that had made her gasp when it was first offered. But...Ann still came first.

She smiled at her again as she left the room. Dreamy, impractical Ann, who persisted in seeing the world through rose-coloured glasses, whereas hers were as clear as crystal—sometimes painfully so.

And Emile, in spite of his youth, had been like her, she thought quietly as she walked through to the tiny lounge. Determined and obdurate and wholly devoted to her sister. When Ann and her Frenchman had decided to get married eight months ago, at the same time as the American offer had materialised, she had had no qualms about entrusting her quiet, gentle, sensitive sister to Emile's care and leaving for the States.

Jacques Challier was waiting in the middle of the room as she entered, his tall, immaculate figure somewhat incongruous against the threadbare carpet, the diminutive two-seater sofa and the old rocking-chair that made up the sum total of the furniture besides the small portable TV on a rickety chest of drawers. A good third of her salary each month had gone straight over the Atlantic into Ann and Emile's joint account, but even so, being two students on a limited budget, they had struggled to get by. But they had been rich in love. Her throat tightened at the thought.

'I'm going to make Ann a cup of tea; would you like one, Mr Challier?' she asked coldly, indicating for him to be seated. She would get through the next few minutes with a modicum of dignity, she thought tersely, in spite of the fact that she would have given the world to scream all the abuse that had been mounting for the last few days into his handsome, superior face.

'Thank you.' He didn't smile. 'That would be most welcome, Miss—?'

'Gosdon—Sandi Gosdon.' She waved her hand at the sofa behind him again. 'Do sit down, Mr Challier. I'm sorry that the furnishings are not quite what you're used to, but—'

'Miss Gosdon, I'm fully aware that at this moment in time you would like nothing more than to wipe all trace of the Challier name from the face of the earth,' he said flatly, his eyes glittering at her sarcasm, 'but don't you think that in the circumstances we could try to communicate?'

'Why?' She faced him directly now, her eyes sparking. 'Exactly why?'

'Because of your sister.'

'She doesn't need you—any of you,' Sandi said tightly. 'The only Challier that mattered to her is dead, so what can you do for her now? And don't mention money,' she warned furiously as he opened his mouth to reply. 'Don't you dare.'

'You think she can live on fresh air?'

How could someone who looked so much like Emile, although admittedly an older version, be so hateful? she asked herself silently as she stared at him with all the dislike and bitterness in her heart evident in her eyes. 'I can look after her.'

'You?' There was a wealth of contempt in his voice, and as he waved a disparaging hand she noticed a heavy gold watch that would have paid the rent on the flat for a year or more gleaming on one tanned wrist. 'I hardly think so, although I am sure you are well intentioned. Ann is twenty years of age, I understand, and you are—what? Twenty-one? Twenty-two? And with the child—'

'Ann's child!' Sandi's voice was shaking with rage.

'And Emile's.' In comparison, his was icy cold.

'But Emile is dead and Ann is alive,' she said tightly. 'And as it happens, Mr Challier, I am twenty-eight years of age and have an extremely highly paid job in America. I can more than adequately support my sister and her child for the next few years.'

'Really?' He didn't move an inch, although she saw the flash of surprise in his eyes before he had time to conceal it.

'Yes, really.' She had seen something else there too— a hot, dark anger, like black lightning, that had turned the handsome face stony hard before a mask had settled over the autocratic features, concealing his thoughts.

So you don't like to be foiled in your plans, Mr Jacques Challier, she thought silently as she stared her dislike. And you don't like me much either. Well, that's good, that's very good—because the only thing that could give me any satisfaction at this moment in time would be to frustrate that cold, logical mind and send you back to your socially élite family with your tail very firmly between your legs!

'And you think it fair—wise—to deny your sister's child the comfort of its father's family?' he asked smoothly after a long, still moment when they faced each other like two gladiators about to enter the ring. 'I understood from Emile that your parents are dead and there are no close relatives. That being the case, do you think one aunt can compensate for the loss of a host of grandparents, aunts, uncles, cousins?'

'If they are Challiers then the answer has to be yes,' she said bitterly.

'But your niece or nephew will bear this hated name, surely?' he asked with deceptive mildness. 'As did its father.'

'I've got no intention of bandying words with you.' She drew herself up to her full five feet five and wished with all her heart that she were a statuesque, model-type six feet, so that she could have glared at him eye to eye. 'I think I've made the position clear.'

'And it would seem I have failed in this respect.' He smiled, but it was a smile utterly without warmth. 'I came here today on behalf of my family to offer our respects to Emile's widow, but now—' He stopped abruptly as he glanced towards the bedroom. 'Now everything has changed.'

'Like hell it has.' She couldn't match his cold, austere bearing or air of ruthless command and she didn't even try. Instead she faced him like a small, enraged lioness, with her teeth all but bared. She knew exactly what he meant. The baby. Ann and Emile's unborn baby. It was that and that alone that had captured his interest.

She had heard about these old and noble families—and the Challiers were certainly that—had heard stories of their obsessional desire for male heirs that sacrificed everything in its path. André, the other brother, had five daughters, and Emile had been of the opinion that Jacques would never marry, was the eternal bachelor—so that left... 'When Emile died all ties with the Challier family were cut—'

'Don't be naïve, Miss Gosdon.'

Now the deep, rich voice was definitely nasty, and as he moved closer, staring down at her from cold, narrowed eyes, a whiff of frighteningly expensive after shave caused her stomach to contract in fear. It spoke of wealth and power and influence, all formidable weapons, but there was something else... A sudden realisation of the

overwhelming maleness of this man, the sensual force
and vigour that were apparent even when he was absolutely still, like now.

'Because I know you aren't. I think it is time for both
of us to acknowledge exactly where we stand, yes?' She
didn't say a word; she couldn't. She just remained frozen
before him like a mouse before a snake. 'My parents are
entitled to know that they will have another grandchild
in the not too distant future—I think even you would
agree with that?'

'Then you think wrong,' she snapped hotly, stung to
speech by his infuriating command. 'And if you're going
to suggest that it would be all sweetness and light on the
Challier side just because Ann's expecting Emile's child,
I don't believe you. As you just pointed out, I'm not
naïve, and there is no way I'm going to stand by and
see her treated as some sort of second-class citizen—'

'I know, I know.' He interrupted her with a raised
hand and sardonic face. 'My family are not worthy to—
what was it? Ah, yes—lick the boots. I have, as you say,
received the message.'

'Good.' She eyed him warily. 'So you accept there is
no point in your family visiting Ann?'

'But there is no question of that.' His voice was cool—
too cool, and the determined set of the hard jaw was
not exactly reassuring either. 'It would be far
more...appropriate for your sister to accompany me to
my parents' home in France and take up residence with
my mother until the child is born.'

'You've got to be joking...' She gazed at him open-
mouthed until his mocking gaze informed her of the fact,
whereupon she shut her mouth with a tight little snap.

'I never joke, Miss Gosdon; I consider it a singular
waste of time,' he said softly, his French accent making
the words attractive even as their content chilled her
blood. 'My family are wealthy and secure and can

provide Ann with all she needs. You would really rather see her have the child in these conditions?'

'These conditions?' She glared at him angrily. 'I can assure you there are a lot worse, Mr Challier. This flat might be small, but it's—'

'No fit place for a Challier to be born,' he said tightly, his face contemptuous.

'But you didn't care whether Emile and Ann were alive or dead this time last week,' she protested furiously. 'And now, just because Ann's pregnant, everything has got to be done as you wish it? You can't force her into something she doesn't want—take her to a strange country with people she doesn't know—'

'Miss Gosdon—' He took a deep breath and suddenly relaxed his big body, sinking down onto the sofa behind him and leaning back with one leg crossed over his knee. He stared up at her with glittering black eyes. 'Shall we have that tea?' he asked smoothly. 'I'm sure Ann is waiting for hers. And perhaps when we have both calmed down we can discuss this matter rationally. I can understand that you are apprehensive, and your concern for your sister does you credit, but there are things you do not understand—things I must explain to you.'

'I . . .' She stared at him helplessly. He obviously had no intention of leaving, and he was too big to manhandle out of the flat, but every instinct in her body was screaming at her to do just that. He was dangerous. Her violet-blue eyes widened at the thought, but it was true. Her sixth sense had told her just that the second she had opened the door to him, and part of her antagonism had been a form of self-protection against the overpowering magnetism that was inherent in the man . . .

But this was no time for fanciful wanderings. She pulled herself together sharply. She had to handle this in the best way she could. He could have his darn tea and then she would listen, very meekly, to everything he said, and agree where necessary, and then she would

usher him out of the flat and never let him or any other
of the Challier brood set foot in the place again.

If it hadn't been for their meanness in cutting Emile
off without a penny towards his education he wouldn't
have had to take that punishingly tiring job which had
ultimately killed him. And his crime? He had married
the woman he loved. A woman they had despised and
loathed whilst refusing even to meet her.

'I'll get the tea,' she said flatly.

He was sitting exactly as she had left him when she
returned with the tea, and, although her stomach muscles
clenched at the sight of his big, relaxed body and dark,
sardonic, handsome face, she betrayed none of her inner
agitation as she carefully set the tray down on the floor—
the flat being devoid of niceties such as coffee-tables and
the like. 'How do you like your tea?' she asked quietly,
without raising her eyes to his face.

'Black.'

She might have guessed. Like his soul. She poured the
tea into a mug and handed it across, taking care not to
come into contact with his flesh. 'There aren't any cups
and saucers,' she said briefly.

'No matter. This is most acceptable.' He leant back
in the seat after reaching for the mug, and after she had
poured her own tea she was forced to lift her gaze to
his, her face expressionless. 'May I call you Sandi?' he
asked softly.

'What?' The hard-won composure fled.

'Your name—may I call you by your name?' he asked
again. 'It is a little ridiculous, this Miss Gosdon and Mr
Challier, do you not think? And we have much to
discuss.'

'I don't think we have anything to—'

'Please.' He raised an authoritative hand and she was
furious at her instant obedience to the command. 'Let
us deal with the immediate problems one by one, Sandi.'

His accent gave her name a life all of its own. 'Ann has her tea?' She nodded silently. 'Then let us talk.

'The first thing I have to say is that my mother is devastated by the turn of events.' She noticed that he didn't mention his father, and wondered why for a fleeting second before he went on. 'I understand Emile's support from my parents was terminated on his marriage?' She nodded again, her eyes tight on his dark face. 'This, I knew nothing about.'

'You didn't?' She shook her head slowly. 'I'm sorry, but I find that very hard to believe. Why wouldn't your parents tell you what they had done?'

'Because they knew I would have paid the cost of Emile's education myself,' he said quietly. 'Sandi...' He shifted in his chair, as though he was finding the conversation difficult. 'There are matters—personal matters—which I find it painful to discuss. Suffice it to say, my parents bitterly regret their action in view of the present circumstances. The knowledge that they will have to live with the consequence of what they have done is punishment enough, surely?'

She shrugged without speaking. There was nothing she could say, after all.

'My brother André and I were told of Emile's relationship with your sister when it first began fifteen months ago, and at that time I warned him to go carefully.'

'I'm sure you did.' Her voice was bitter and tight, and he shook his dark head at the pain and contempt in her face.

'Not for the reason you imagine,' he said quietly.

'No?' She eyed him hotly. 'What was the reason, then?'

'I am not at liberty to say.'

'Oh, really!' She turned away with a gesture of contempt. 'This is ridiculous. I don't believe—'

'The reason was a good one—or it seemed so at the time,' he said levelly. 'When matters advanced and Emile told the family that he intended to marry your sister it was not well received, as you know. My brother André and I were of the opinion that once it was *fait accompli* the natural order of things would take their course. Time is a great healer—'

'Of what?' she asked tightly. 'The fact that Emile had married so far beneath him in your parents' eyes? Or was it that Ann is not French? I understand André's wife is the daughter of a count. I suppose she was welcomed with open arms!'

'We are not discussing Odile—'

'We're not *discussing* anything at all,' she said angrily. 'You're talking *at* me without telling me anything substantial. Look, I really think it would be better if you left—'

'I have no intention of leaving, Sandi.' The dark eyes were chips of black glass as they stared into hers. 'And you will listen to everything I have to say. There are certain confidences that are not mine to divulge, but once Ann meets my family—'

'*If* Ann meets your family,' she corrected tightly. 'The decision is hers, after all.'

'Quite.' The black eyes bored into hers. 'Hers and hers alone. I am glad you mentioned that.' His meaning was unmistakable, and she flushed hotly before meeting the challenge.

'You're quite right,' she said as coolly as she could, considering that the urge to rise and empty her tea over his immaculate head was fierce. 'If it was left to me Ann would never meet any of you, but she is a grown woman in her own right and, although I shall make my opinion clear, the final decision will be hers. She loved Emile very much and your parents hurt him badly. Whether that will colour her judgement I don't know.'

'He also loved them very much, you know,' Jacques said softly. 'As they did him. I am thirty-six years of age and André is thirty-four. Emile was the baby of the family, the late arrival, and my mother doted on him.'

'She had a funny way of showing it.' She couldn't have stopped herself speaking if her life had depended on it, but strangely he didn't react as she had expected—with anger and blazing indignation. Instead the black eyes narrowed still further on her flushed face and he rose slowly, moving across the room to stand in front of her. She, too, rose—she was at a distinct disadvantage seated as she was in the old rocking-chair—and raised her chin as she stared back into the handsome, cold face watching her so closely.

'All this righteous scorn and resentment . . .' he muttered softly as his eyes stroked over her hot face, their darkness unfathomable. 'You give the appearance of being hard and worldly—one would even think that you have worked at this image.' She said nothing, fear at his intuitiveness rendering her dumb. 'But your eyes tell another story,' he continued quietly. 'A quite different one. Why this hard shell, Sandi Gosdon? What has happened in your twenty-eight years to make you so hostile, so ready to see the dark side?'

'I am seeing what's under my nose,' she retorted stiffly, 'and I don't like being soft-soaped. If, in your opinion, that makes me hard and worldly, then so be it.'

'I didn't say I thought you were hard and worldly,' he corrected softly. 'I said that I believe this is the image you like to project. I am wrong in this supposition?'

'Quite wrong.' She glared at him angrily and forced her eyes not to flicker at the lie. And it wasn't a lie, not really. After what she'd been through, after Ian, she preferred to keep the world in general and men in particular at arm's length. There was nothing wrong in that, was there?

He smiled slowly, as though she had confirmed his opinion rather than denied it. 'I will return this evening, and then I would like to speak to Ann directly—if I may?' he said quietly.

'Ann will see things as I do.' Sandi's heart gave a little jump as she spoke. Since she had been able to toddle her sister had been the easiest person in the world to manipulate—her sensitive gentle nature shying away from any kind of confrontation or disagreement. She would be putty in this man's hands, even without him having a head start in looking so startlingly like Emile.

'We will see.' The deep brown, almost black eyes were suddenly ruthless. 'But I *will* put my case to your sister, Sandi, with or without your blessing. In this I shall be most determined; you understand me?'

'Perfectly,' she ground out through clenched teeth.

'Good.' He smiled again as he held out his hand in farewell, but for the life of her she couldn't voluntarily respond to the goodwill gesture.

She didn't want to touch him. Her mind raced at the thought. And yet he was handsome—probably over-whelmingly so to some females—but not to her. Oh, no, not to her. She had had her fingers burnt too badly by men who thought they only had to smile and the world rocked on its axis.

'I don't bite, Miss Sandi Gosdon.' The dark voice was mocking and amused, and it was the thread of laughter in the deep tones that brought her hand out to meet his.

'I'm sure you don't, Mr Challier,' she said coldly.

'Till this evening, then.' His flesh was warm and firm as it enfolded hers, and as he raised her small hand to his lips for a fleeting moment an electric shock shot up her arm, causing her to snatch her hand away as though he had burnt her. For a split second she saw surprise in the dark face, and then it closed against her, his eyes hooded and remote.

'I shall return at seven,' he said coolly. 'Please do not think of advising your sister not to be here. It would be most unwise.'

'Really?' So he was a mind-reader as well?

'Really.' He walked towards the door, turning in the doorway to survey her through narrowed eyes. 'It is only fair to warn you that I am a stubborn man—stubborn and determined. And I always get exactly what I want.'

'But do you always get what you deserve, Mr Challier?' she asked with honeyed sweetness, looking straight into the autocratic face.

For a moment she thought she had gone too far as he stared back at her, a small flame glowing in the depths of the black eyes, but then the cold, beautifully shaped mouth twisted in an amused smile and he shrugged slowly. 'Now, of that I am not sure,' he murmured softly as his gaze wandered over her hair and face. 'Perhaps I will be able to give you an answer to that one day—who knows?' He smiled again, his dark maleness intimidating and virile in the small room, and as her breath caught in her throat she realised that the palms of her hands were damp. With what? Fright? Sexual attraction? Panic?

But she wouldn't let herself feel any of those emotions for a man like him, she thought angrily. What use was the past, in all its painfulness, if she hadn't learnt well from it? 'I doubt it,' she said, and stared back at him, unaware of how young she looked in the middle of the small room, a ray of sunlight from the narrow window behind her turning her hair to glowing gold and her eyes to a deep, stormy blue. 'I would think our paths won't cross again after today.'

'Perhaps.' He shrugged again and turned to leave. 'And perhaps not. Life has a way of surprising us when we least expect it. Till seven . . .'

As she heard the front door of the flat close she stood perfectly still, her hands clenched tight against her sides and her heart pounding furiously. Oh, she knew all about surprises, she thought bitterly. He'd be amazed at how much she knew. She shut her eyes to banish the images of the past that were suddenly stark and savage on the screen of her mind, and when Ann called, her voice nervous and faint from the bedroom, it was a relief to come back to the present and hurry to her sister's side.

CHAPTER TWO

WHEN Jacques Challier returned at seven all Sandi's worst fears were realised. He was charm itself as he talked to Ann, his voice persuasive and soft as he explained how distraught and stunned his parents—his mother in particular—were at their youngest son's untimely death.

Their remorse at the way things had turned out, their sorrow for his young widow and their bitter-sweet joy on hearing of their future grandchild from Jacques that afternoon—all was relayed with great sensitivity and appeal, and, in Sandi's eyes at least, utter ruthlessness to further his own ends. He worked on Ann like a master musician with his instrument until he had her eating out of his hand, her large blue eyes dark with sympathy and distress and her mouth soft with compassion.

'Emile would have wanted you to be with his family at this time,' Jacques said quietly, 'even though you perhaps feel you can't forgive us for the way we have behaved. I can understand that you blame us for his death—'

'No, not really.' Ann twisted uncomfortably. 'Maybe at first, but not now. It was an accident, I know that—but he had got so tired, you see, working for his finals all day and with the job at night. But we needed the money. Even with what Sandi sent us—'

'You sent them money?' Jacques asked sharply, turning to Sandi, who was standing to one side of the sofa, looking down at him with bitter eyes as she watched the little scene in front of her.

'Of course.' She glared at him without explaining further.

'Even with what Sandi sent us we couldn't manage,' Ann continued quietly. 'Not once I'd left the university and my grant had stopped.'

'Ann's pregnancy was difficult from the outset,' Sandi said flatly. 'There was no way she could continue to work for her degree, although she and Emile had planned that she would return to her studies later—once the baby was born and he had finished university and had a job.'

'I see.' Jacques turned to Ann again, taking one of her hands in his. 'The rest of the family did not know that Emile's support had stopped, Ann; please believe that. And when I spoke to my mother this afternoon she asked me to tell you the reason why they took this step—this foolish step that they now regret so much. It is a matter of great delicacy, and I would be grateful if you would not speak of it to anyone.'

'I'll get some coffee—'

'No, please, Sandi.' He quickly stopped her move to leave the room. 'It is necessary that you understand this, for the future—yes?'

No, she thought tightly, but nevertheless she found herself sitting gingerly on the rocking-chair, facing them both as he talked.

'When Emile informed my parents that you were going to get married they were upset—my mother particularly so,' Jacques said slowly. 'She thought if his grant was threatened he would see what she considered to be reason and put off the wedding until he had finished university. In that way she was hoping this relationship between you would perhaps fail the test of time and come to nothing.

'She was concerned about the result a marriage might have on his studies, also that the two of you were so young, but there was another, more important reason that overshadowed all that.' He paused, rising from the sofa where he had been sitting next to Ann and moving to stand with his back towards them as he looked out of the window into the grimy London street below.

'Two years ago my father was foolish enough to have an *amour* with a young English girl who had recently come to work for us,' he said expressionlessly. 'And even more foolishly he was indiscreet enough for my mother to suspect what was happening. She confronted my father, who admitted the affair and immediately agreed to end the liaison.

'But the damage, as far as my mother was concerned, was done. She suffered a nervous breakdown from which even now she is not fully recovered.

'As my father's business partner, I was told the full facts, but no one else in the family—including André and Emile—had any idea what had caused my mother's illness. This, both my mother and father wanted. When Emile fell in love with you so soon after all this had happened she just couldn't—how do you say?—handle it.' Jacques turned to face both women now, but his face could have been carved in stone, so devoid was it of any visible emotion.

'Her behaviour at this time was not rational or wise, but she was still suffering greatly and my father was consumed by guilt—he still is, I think. This girl had flattered and cajoled him, persuaded him into the alliance, but it was a thing of the flesh, not the heart. She was sent packing with a cheque which amply soothed her ruffled feathers.' Now a flash of searing bitterness lit the black eyes for a brief moment. 'And my mother has tried to pick up the pieces of a life which has been smashed apart. She wants you to know this not so that you will excuse her actions, but perhaps understand them.' He was standing very straight and stiff, his face set and proud.

'I—' Sandi saw Ann take a gulp and swallow before she tried to speak again. 'I'm so sorry, Jacques; she must have been very hurt.'

He nodded grimly. 'She was.' The black eyes narrowed on Ann's pale face. 'But nothing could compare to the loss of her child. My father and I have not told her the full facts of the accident. She thinks merely that Emile was killed whilst riding in a car. If she knew the accident was a direct result of the job he had taken to make ends meet—'

'I won't tell her,' Ann responded quickly. 'There is no point, after all, and Emile wouldn't have wanted it.'

'Thank you.' Jacques nodded quietly, his eyes flashing to Sandi's face as she watched them.

She had been as shocked as Ann at the revelation, but her mistrust of the Challier family as a whole, and Jacques Challier in particular, was unaffected by his explanation—although she couldn't have explained why. She couldn't help feeling that, genuine though his account of the circumstances obviously was, he was using it to persuade Ann to do exactly what he wanted. And his next words confirmed her fears.

'And now I must ask you an even greater service. My mother would very much like to meet you, to speak to you herself. Would you accompany me to France for this purpose?'

'I—' Ann's eyes shot to Sandi. 'I don't think so. I haven't been feeling too well, and there's the baby—'

'All the more reason to be in the comfort and safety of my parents' home,' Jacques returned smoothly. 'Their doctor is excellent and the nearest hospital is just a few miles away—you would receive exemplary care, should it prove necessary. Here the facilities are a little...basic?' His face was expressionless but his meaning clear. 'And I understand Sandi has a demanding job in the States. I'm sure she would rest better at nights knowing you were well taken care of.'

'I told you, I'm going to look after Ann,' Sandi said tightly, deciding she had had more than enough of this subtle manoeuvring. 'There is no question that she would be alone.'

'But your work?' Jacques enquired with suspect concern, his eyes gleaming as they took in her angry face. 'Surely this could prove difficult? If you stay in England with Ann this must put your job in jeopardy, and if she returns with you to America she will have long periods of being left alone.'

'A certain amount of my work is done from home—'

'But not all of it.' He stared at her, his face impassive as he tied her up in knots. 'You would not be able to relax when you were not with her, whereas in France there would be my mother and the servants—'

'Don't tell me what I would or wouldn't be able to do,' Sandi shot back immediately. 'If it's necessary I can resign.'

'Oh, no, Sandi!' Even as her sister spoke Sandi realised she had played right into Jacques's very capable hands. The worst thing she could have done was suggest that there might be a possibility of her leaving her job. Ann knew how she had worked for her success, how thrilled she had been with her new appointment, and her sister's soft heart wouldn't be able to bear the thought of it all being lost—especially as she was aware of the therapy it had provided after Ian... 'Please, I don't want you to worry about me any more—and besides, I'd like to meet Emile's parents. Really.'

'Ann—'

'I mean it, Sandi.' Ann cut into her protest with un-usual firmness. 'It's got to happen sooner or later, and perhaps it's best to meet them now. You know I'm not very good at facing things, but with the baby...' She shook her head slowly. 'It's only natural they would want to see it when it's born, and I'd prefer to meet them first. I'll just come for a few days, Jacques.' She turned to the tall, dark man who had remained silent through the little exchange. 'If that's all right?'

'Of course.' He bowed his head in a little gesture that was very French. 'You must stay as long as you wish.'

Once Ann was out there she would be kept there—at least until the baby was born, Sandi thought darkly. Couldn't her sister see what was happening? She looked into Ann's pale, lovely face thoughtfully. Or maybe it was easier for her not to. Ann had always been so very good at hiding her head in the sand.

'That is settled, then.' Jacques's eyes mocked her as he looked down at her sitting so stiff with rage in the rocking-chair. 'If it fits in with your plans, perhaps you would like to accompany Ann to France? I'm sure she would find that most...reassuring.'

'Sandi? Could you?' Ann's voice was eager.

'Of course.' She smiled at her sister but her eyes changed to splintered blue when they met Jacques's. 'I've taken some leave to sort things out here.'

'Excellent.' The cold voice held a thread of amusement that made her want to kick him—hard. 'Then perhaps if I could suggest I pick you up tomorrow afternoon, say, two o'clock? That should give you time to make all the necessary domestic arrangements and organise passports and so on. I do not think it wise that Ann flies at this time, you agree?'

She nodded silently, having been about to make that point herself.

'My parents' château is only a few hours' drive from the Channel, so this will not prove a problem. I will arrange to have one of the cars waiting for us.'

Sandi continued to stare at him, her thoughts whirling. She was experiencing the most awful sense of *déjà vu*. This could have been Ian talking. Ian, with his forceful, cool air of authority that she had thought so attractive at the time and which had hidden such treachery. Ian...his big body lean and virile, confident of his power to subject and subdue, to command without question. And she had fallen for it. Utterly. And how she had paid for her naïvety...

'Sandi?' She came back to the present with a violent sense of having been on a nightmarish journey as Ann touched her arm tentatively. 'Are you all right?'

'I'm fine.' She forced a quick smile and turned away from the intent pair of dark eyes across the room. 'I'll get that coffee now.'

When, a few moments later, she heard the door to the tiny lounge open and close she looked up from the coffee-cups expecting to see Ann in the doorway, her mouth already open to order her back to her chair. 'Can I help at all?' Jacques's undeniably attractive smile did not reach the glittering blackness of his eyes.

'No.' She qualified the blunt refusal with a quick shake of her head. 'No, thank you. I can manage, Mr Challier.'

'Of this I have no doubt.' She glanced across at him once, her eyes distant, before resuming the preparation of the tray. 'You do not think it appropriate that we drop this formality in view of developments?' he asked quietly after a long moment of silence.

'Developments?' she asked coldly, raising her head to meet his dark gaze. 'If you mean by that the fact that my sister and I shall be guests in your home, I hardly see—'

'Not my home, Sandi.' The deep voice was infuriatingly smooth. 'My parents' home. I have my own establishment some distance away. But, of course, if you would prefer to stay with me...?' Her face spoke volumes and he chuckled huskily, shaking his head as he leant lazily against the doorpost. 'What a bad-tempered little pussy-cat you are...' he drawled thoughtfully. 'All claws and teeth.'

'Not at all.' She drew herself up to her full height and spoke through clenched teeth. 'Just because I don't happen to approve of your blackmailing technique—'

'Blackmail? This is not a nice word,' he reproved softly.

'It's not a nice act,' she returned tersely.

'And this is how you see my family's wish to help your sister?' he asked slowly. 'As something intimidating? Suspect?' There was a grimness about the handsome face now that made her hesitate for a moment, but then she shook off its menacing effect and spoke her mind.

'Considering that up to a few hours ago the Challier name was synonymous with rejection and pain, how do you expect me to feel?' she asked tensely. 'Ann is six months pregnant, and in all that time not one of your family has even sent a postcard!'

'But Ann is prepared to be reasonable—'

'Ann is too trusting,' she said flatly.

'And you—you are not,' he stated quietly, moving to stand in front of her and holding her eyes with his own in a vice-like grip she was powerless to break. His bronzed skin, the smooth blackness of his hair, the big, lean body that was intimidatingly male—it all served to hold her mesmerised under the dark, glittering gaze as he leant towards her. 'What was his name, Sandi—this man who has put the fear and mistrust in those beautiful blue eyes? Do you still love him?'

'I don't know what you're talking about.' She had wanted her voice to be acidic, but it was merely shaky.

'No?' He lifted her chin with the tip of one finger and she felt the contact right down to her toes. 'From the first moment we met you have been fighting me—and do not tell me it is because of Ann, because then I would have to call you a liar.' His face was close now, too close, the firm, sensual mouth an inch or two from hers. 'Is it because you sense I want to do this?'

She was totally unprepared for the feel of his lips on hers, standing stunned for one breathtaking moment as his mouth took hers and then jerking away so violently that she felt her neck muscles snap.

'How dare you?' She backed another step before bringing her hand to her mouth in a harsh scrubbing action. 'How *dare* you?'

'I dared because I wanted to, very much,' he said softly.

'And that makes it all right?' she asked scathingly as pure rage flowed through her veins. 'You see, you like, you take—is that it? The original macho man? Well, I'm immune to all such rubbish—so you can just forget that old line and you can keep your hands off me too. You ever try a number like that again—'

'*Zut!*' The oath was soft but intense. 'It was merely a kiss.'

'I know what it was,' she answered tightly, 'and I'm not interested, OK? Is that plain enough?'

He growled something under his breath and she was heartily glad that she knew no French. 'I was not asking you to come into my bed,' he said darkly, 'or even into my life. The kiss was an acknowledgement of your beauty, of the age-old attraction between male and female—'

'Oh, spare me...' She glared at him furiously. 'How many other poor sops have you tried this one on? I really can't believe—'

'Miss Gosdon, if you say one more word I really think I will not be responsible for my actions.' She could see that he was fighting for control under that icy exterior and it gave her enormous satisfaction. Just to have rocked that amazingly arrogant stance a little, to have punctured that thick male skin and imperious self-esteem, was wonderfully gratifying. For a moment it was Ian's face there in front of her, his hard, lean body that was held so stiffly to attention. And then the image faded, and with it her rage as she heard Ann call from the lounge.

'Sandi?'

'I don't want anything else to upset Ann,' she said quickly as she heard the lounge door open. 'She's been through more than enough—'

'What on earth are you doing out here?' Ann's voice held more than a touch of apprehension although her face was smiling as she appeared in the open doorway, her eyes darting from Jacques's face to Sandi's.

'I—' Sandi found that her mind was a complete blank.

'Your sister was telling me about her work,' Jacques said easily at her side, his voice cool and lazy and his manner relaxed. 'You must be very proud of her.'

'Oh, I am.' Ann smiled back at him, completely reassured. 'Sandi left university to get a job when Mum and Dad died so we could stay together. She's worked her way up from the bottom rung of the ladder, and she deserves everything she gets.'

'Really...?' Jacques's voice was very dry.

'Did she tell you how...?'

Sandi let Ann lead him back into the lounge, and once she was alone leant back against the painted wood cupboards in the very basic kitchen. The nerve of the man, kissing her like that! Who on earth did he think he was— God's gift to womankind?

The glug of the coffee-maker reminded her of the task in hand, and she quickly finished setting the tray and poured three cups of coffee once the machine was ready. Well, here was one woman who wasn't going to melt into a little pool at his feet—although that was obviously what the little charade had been all about. Were there still women about in the world who fell for old lines like that?

It was much later, as she lay wide awake at Ann's side watching the bedside clock tick the minutes and hours away, that she gave in to the searing memories from the past that had been at the forefront of her mind since she had first set eyes on Jacques Challier. Of course there were still women who were taken in by a handsome face and a soft, tender voice—she of all people should know that.

Once the floodgate in her mind was open there was no stopping the tide...

She had been almost twenty-five years of age when she had met Ian Mortimer, and as innocent as a babe. They had met through a friend of a friend at one of the numerous advertising parties that were commonplace in London, and from the first moment his smoky grey eyes had smiled into hers she had been lost. His charm had been considerable, his technique polished to perfection, and she had never doubted one thing he had told her about himself—even though, with hindsight, there had been plenty of question marks.

Ann hadn't liked him. Sandi shut her eyes for a moment in the darkness. Funny, that, when you considered that Ann usually liked everyone. But she hadn't liked Ian Mortimer, and how right she had been.

They had been together for four months when he'd asked her to marry him, and that had been accomplished, via the registry office, within weeks. Their joint bank account had been a declaration of their love and trust, Ian had assured her, despite the fact that all the money in it had come from the account she'd had from her half-share of her parents' estate, Ann's portion being held in trust until her sister reached the age of twenty-one.

Sandi twisted restlessly and then froze as the movement disturbed Ann's steady, regular breathing at her side. Although her sister had cried herself to sleep in the same way she had done each night since Sandi had arrived back in England, she had slipped into a deep slumber within minutes—which was a definite improvement on all the previous nights and one that Sandi wanted to continue.

That awful morning... Her thoughts drifted back to the sunny May morning, almost exactly three years ago, when she had run to answer the ring of the bell at the front door of the small flat she and Ian had been renting. Ann had already left for college and she had been late for work, but the thought that it might be Ian, due back that day from the business trip that had taken him away for two weeks, had put wings on her feet. He'd forgotten his key again, she'd thought happily as she'd swung open the door. He had a head like a sieve...

But it hadn't been Ian. The tall, attractive woman who had faced her had had short dark hair and gentle brown eyes, and the eyes had continued to be gentle as she had begun to talk. It was strange that her world had been devastated by someone with such gentle eyes...

'Mrs Mortimer?' The woman held out her hand. 'How do you do? My name is Carol Prescott. I don't suppose Ian's told you about me?'

'Ian...?' Sandi shook her head slowly. 'No, I'm sorry. You know my husband?'

'Unfortunately.' Sandi was nonplussed by the grimness in the soft voice. 'Yes, unfortunately I do. Look, we really need to talk. Can I come in a minute?'

'Well, I'm already late for work—'

'This won't wait, Mrs Mortimer.' The woman smiled regretfully. 'And please believe me, I am really very, very sorry.'

And so the nightmare began. It appeared that her husband, wonderful, dashing Ian, with his liquid grey eyes and dark, romantic good looks, was a confidence trickster of the first order. Carol Prescott had brought a sheaf of papers with her—a history of his activities over the past few years that she had made it her business to investigate.

It made sickening reading. Ian preyed on young, and in some cases not so young women who had a certain amount of money—the amounts ranging from a few thousand to much higher figures in one or two cases—making them believe he loved them and then departing with his ill-gotten gains once he had milked each one dry. His explanations were various—business problems, an ill mother, a temporary hold-up in funds—but the end result was always the same. A broken-hearted woman with no Ian and no money.

'But I don't understand...' Sandi's heart was thudding like a drum as she faced Carol Prescott in the sun-filled lounge. 'Why haven't the police got involved if all you say is true?'

'It's true,' Carol replied quietly, 'and the police *are* involved—at least in two cases where Ian forged signatures. As for the others...' She shrugged bitterly. 'If silly women want to make gifts of money or jewellery to their current boyfriend that's between the two of them, according to officialdom. The police are busy—they haven't got time to chase all over England searching for one man, besides which he uses a wide variety of names which makes everything more difficult.'

'But why—?' Sandi stopped abruptly as the full realisation of what was happening to her began to make itself felt and the room swam and dipped. 'I mean—'

'Why am I on this crusade?' Carol asked flatly. 'Because someone had to do it—someone had to try and stop him. I met him five years ago, just after my mother had died and left me the house and a tidy amount in the bank. Ian wormed all the money out of me, and when I began to suspect that something wasn't right he disappeared one night with all my mother's jewellery—even her wedding ring. That's what I really can't forgive him for.'

Her eyes were deep wells of pain as she stared at Sandi. 'A solicitor friend with a million and one contacts helped me begin to search for him, and then we discovered a veritable can of worms. He's in his thirties now, and he's been at this game since he was fresh out of school.'

'But—' Sandi took a deep breath and then forced herself to speak although her throat was dry and her chest tight. 'But we're married. Or is that a lie too? Is he already married to someone else?'

'No, you're legally married,' Carol said quietly. 'Although frankly, if I were you, I'd prefer that to be false too. As far as I know he's never actually married anyone before—I don't think he's had to, to be honest. Most women fall for him so badly they can't wait to shower him with gifts. Have you given him much?' she asked gently.

'No.' Sandi shook her head slowly. 'I haven't given him anything.' But he *had* wanted her to live with him, wanted her to be his lover. It had been she who had held out for marriage, she thought blindly, wanting to give herself to him for the first time on her wedding night, wanting him to be the first and only. Oh... She shut her eyes tight. Let this be a mistake, she prayed. A terrible, ghastly mistake. He couldn't have done all this; he couldn't.

'Joint account?'

Sandi opened her eyes wide at the quiet voice. 'What?'

'Have you a joint account?' Carol asked patiently, shaking her head at Sandi's nod. 'And where's Ian now?'

'On a business trip...' Sandi's voice trailed away.

'There is no business,' Carol said softly, 'and I think he knew I was closing in on him—which meant the police would be informed as to his whereabouts. I think you'd better get on to the bank...'

The bank manager was very kind when she saw him later that morning. He said that he had wondered why she and her husband had decided to close the account so abruptly, but Mr Mortimer had explained that they were moving abroad. He hoped everything had gone through satisfactorily.

Twenty thousand pounds. Was it worth ruining someone's life for twenty thousand pounds? she thought now helplessly. Obviously Ian had thought so. He had vanished without trace.

She couldn't bear to brood on the months that had followed. Without Ann she wouldn't have got through. But by the time she had started to pick up the pieces, six months later, life was beginning to return to something like normality. Which had made that other knock on the door so much harder, somehow.

'Mrs Mortimer? Mrs Ian Mortimer?' The policeman and policewoman had been very kind too, she remembered with painful irony. 'It's about your husband. I'm very sorry to have to tell you...'

Ian had died in a drowning accident off the coast of France while staying on his current girlfriend's yacht. Apparently Sandi's name had been found among his papers. He had had exactly five hundred pounds to his name when he had died. Most of her twenty thousand had gone on riotous living and expensive presents to his new fiancée, who was worth a mint, so it had appeared. How exactly he had planned to marry her too wasn't clear.

Perhaps he wouldn't have gone through with it—who knew? And who cared? She shook her head in the warm darkness. But that final blow had welded the lock and key onto the door of her heart for ever.

Never again would she trust a man, any man, be he rich or poor. Ian had killed the happy, trusting girl she had once been as completely as if he had driven a knife through her heart. And the new Sandi Gosdon? She was her own woman, utterly and totally, and that was the way she intended to remain. No romances, no liaisons, no involvement.

She shook her head as hot tears coursed down her face. Never again. That one savage encounter with love had taught her one thing—she couldn't trust her own heart and still less any man. Her career would be her life, and with that she would be content. Content? The word mocked her, but she thrust the weakness back into the recesses of her mind. She *would* be content. She'd have to be. It was the only course open to her now.

CHAPTER THREE

'WE WILL stop shortly for some refreshments.' Jacques glanced at Sandi briefly before his gaze moved to the mirror, in which he could see Ann stretched out on the back seat of the big car. 'You are comfortable, Ann?' he asked politely.

'I'm fine,' Ann answered drowsily.

They had been travelling for two hours through the lush French countryside on their way to the Challier château in the Loire Valley, and Ann was beginning to show the strain of the journey—although she was bearing up far better than Sandi had anticipated. The May evening was warm and still showing to full advantage the green pastures, the colourful orchards and vine-yards, the old towns with their slate roofs and the spec-tacularly beautiful châteaux. The powerful Mercedes that had been waiting for them on the other side of the Channel ate up the miles with little effort.

It had been sensible for Ann to stretch out on the back seat with her legs raised—her ankles were swollen most days now—but Sandi had been less than comfortable when she'd realised that that meant she would be sitting in close proximity to Jacques in the front of the car. And although she hadn't said a word he had known.

She glanced at him now as he sat, big and dark, at her side. Yes, he had known. The deep brown eyes had glittered with silent amusement and there had been a ruthless twist to his mouth that had told her he was en-joying every moment of her discomfiture.

Why did he affect her so badly? She forced herself to concentrate on the natural beauty of the French

43

countryside. She had thought no man would ever affect her again after Ian, and until Jacques no man had. Everything about him grated on her. Everything.

She bit her lower lip hard. Even when he was being solicitous over Ann the dark power of the man was evident, like a great wild beast that had temporarily sheathed its razor-sharp claws. He was arrogant and imperious and utterly sure of himself and the authority he commanded, and since that incident in Ann's kitchen Sandi had been unable to wipe the feel of his mouth on hers from her consciousness. It was driving her *crazy*. She wanted to be aloof and detached, to pretend he didn't exist, but Jacques Challier was not a man one could ignore.

Thank goodness he had his own home, separate from his parents'. She clung onto the thought like a lifebelt. Hopefully, after this one torturous journey, she wouldn't have to be in his company again.

'I was going to stop at the little tavern down there, but it looks as though Ann has fallen asleep.' His voice was soft and deep at her side, rich and attractive with its broken accent. 'You are happy to carry on with the journey, Sandi?'

'Yes, of course.' She forced a stiff smile from somewhere as she glanced his way, and then wished she hadn't as the hard profile did strange things to her nerves that both alarmed and surprised her.

The way Ian had treated her, the fact that he had taken her youth and her innocence and then used her as carelessly as an old glove, to be tossed away once he had got what he really wanted, had caused a humiliation and debasement so deep that it had taken her months to be able to look in the mirror again with any sense of self-worth. She didn't want to feel anything for any man ever again, and even this... awareness of Emile's brother was frightening.

'It is still some way to the château; couldn't you try to relax a little?' His voice was cool and quiet. 'Even a Frenchman would not try to take a woman against her will in a car travelling at seventy miles an hour when he is the driver.' He glanced at her briefly, and although she didn't turn her head to look at him the black eyes burnt her flesh.

'Don't be ridiculous—'

He cut off her soft but furious voice with a raised hand. 'We do not seem to have—how you say?—hit it off—yes?' he said quietly. 'This is unfortunate, but I am sure we can both live with it. However, the present situation between my mother and Ann is a delicate one and I do not want further complications. My mother has suffered enough—'

'And what about Ann?' She was too enraged now to feel any emotion other than anger. 'She's lost her husband—'

'And my mother has lost her son,' he said grimly.

'And whose fault was that?' The second the words had left her lips she was horrified at their content, but it was too late. The dark face hardened into pure granite and his tone was icy when he spoke.

'Her suffering equals her crime; of that I can assure you. If you want your pound of flesh you will have it when you see my mother's face.'

'I don't want any pound of flesh,' she said bleakly, unaware of the throb of pain in her voice. She had experienced enough suffering in the last three years to last a lifetime; she wouldn't wish such an emotion on any living soul.

He glanced at her swiftly, his eyes narrowing on the taut line of her mouth before his gaze returned to the road. 'No?' He waited a moment but she didn't speak. 'Then perhaps a compromise? We will both do our best to be civil to each other and let the grown-ups sort out their own difficulties?'

He was trying to lighten the situation and she was grateful for it, but just for a moment she couldn't respond, fighting as she was to hold back the flood of tears that was threatening to erupt. 'Yes...' When she did speak her voice was a mere whisper.

'Then this is a deal.' His teeth flashed white in his face as he glanced her way once more, his smile dying at the look on her face as she stared ahead. 'Sandi?' He reached out a hand to touch hers for a fleeting second before returning it to the steering wheel. 'You are OK?'

'I'm fine.' Control, control... What was the matter with her anyway? She'd got her life back the way she wanted it—things had been wonderful before Emile's death. It was that—her sorrow for Ann and her deep sadness for her young husband who had had his life cut short so abruptly. It was enough to make anyone desolate.

In spite of their tentative agreement they continued for the next hour or so in a silence that was anything but comfortable, and Sandi breathed a sigh of relief once Ann woke. 'Have I been asleep?' Ann asked apologetically. 'I'm sorry; I didn't mean to.'

'No problem,' Jacques said easily. 'You are perhaps ready for some refreshment now?'

'I'd love a long, cool drink,' Ann answered gratefully.

They stopped at a small country hotel with a pretty beamed restaurant, and a flower-filled courtyard with a fountain that led directly from the dining area, sitting for a while in the dusky perfumed air with their drinks before returning to the restaurant for their meal, which was simple but delicious.

Sandi was aware of one or two interested glances in their direction. The tall, dark, handsome Frenchman and the two small, blonde and obviously English women had obviously caused a little stir among the locals. They probably thought Ann was Jacques's pregnant wife, Sandi thought with a wry twist to her mouth. And what did that make her? The gooseberry? But she was more than happy to be the gooseberry in this case, she told herself drily. More than happy.

Jacques entertained the two women with an easy courtesy and lazy humour that was dangerously attractive—or would have been if she hadn't known better, Sandi thought cynically. After the meal he escorted them back to the car with a hand on each of their waists, and, light though the contact was, Sandi was inexpressibly thankful when it ceased.

'And now we drive to the Château des Rêves, yes?' Jacques turned to smile at Ann after settling her on the back seat of the car again, and then the dark, glittering gaze moved to Sandi's face at the side of him.

'Château des Rêves?' Ann asked, a note of interest in her voice.

'The castle of dreams,' Jacques replied quietly. 'My parents' house is very beautiful, as you will see—something of a fairy tale, in fact—and dates back to the fourteenth century. I was most fortunate to be brought up in such a place.'

'Emile loved his home,' Ann said quietly from behind them. 'But after...everything that happened he found it difficult to talk about France.'

'This is understandable.' Jacques turned to give her a swift smile before starting the car and drawing carefully out of the small car park. 'I hope you will love it as much as he did.'

I just bet you do, Sandi thought silently at his side. It would make the job of persuading Ann to stay in France until the baby was born so much easier...

The night sky was like black velvet by the time they reached the Loire Valley, but the air was still warm and moist from the heat of the day, without the chill that would have been evident in England. Jacques drove the big car off the main road on which they had been travelling and onto a long drive lined on either side by

massive oak trees. After a full minute Sandi saw the
spires and turrets of a great house in the distance, but
the darkness shrouded the image, the moon merely a
thin hollow of light over the sleeping landscape.

They approached a high stone wall in which vast iron
gates stood open and ready to attention as they passed
through, and immediately a host of lights were triggered
on each side of the drive, lighting the night as brightly
as if it were day.

'The château,' Jacques said briefly, indicating the
enormous sculptured building of honeyed stone in the
distance that was the epitome of all the magic castles
that one heard and read about in childhood rolled into
one. Spires and turrets, arches and fine lace balconies
all joined with breathtaking affect in the old château,
its curves and arcs majestic and proud against the black
sky beyond.

'It's beautiful,' Ann breathed from behind them.

'It's greedy.' Jacques smiled at her wide-eyed face in
the mirror. 'It costs a fortune to maintain, but it's been
in the family for generations—my father was born in
one of the bedrooms on the second floor.'

He brought the car to a standstill on the vast drive
and turned directly to Sandi as he cut the engine. 'What
do you think?' he asked quietly as he waved towards the
château. 'Do you approve?'

'One could hardly disapprove of such a lovely
building,' she said carefully. 'I'm amazed you decided
to leave. How long have you had your own house?'

'Eight years.' Anything else he might have been about
to say was lost as the enormous carved oak doors opened
and a small, slim, exquisitely dressed woman appeared
in the lighted doorway, with several other people just
behind her.

'My mother,' Jacques said quietly. 'André and his
family live in one of the wings of the house, so I'm afraid
it will be the family *en masse* tonight.' He opened his

door, moving round to the other side of the car and opening both Ann's door and her own and helping them to alight.

'Maman—Ann and Sandi.' He took Ann's arm and ushered her forward slightly in front of Sandi, his hand moving protectively to her waist as he sensed her hesitation. 'Ann, this is your mother-in-law.'

'Ann...' Madame Challier's dark brown eyes fastened on Ann's face, and no one could have failed to read the muted appeal in their depths. 'Thank you for coming, my dear. I'm really so sorry—' Her voice broke and she shook her head helplessly. 'You look exhausted— I think...'

As the soft voice floundered again Sandi saw Jacques stiffen, but Ann was there in front of him, reaching out to the woman who had caused her such misery and holding her close for a long moment. 'I'm so sorry...' There was a sob in Jacques's mother's voice now. 'Can you ever forgive us for the way we have behaved?'

'Come on into the house, Maman.' As Jacques motioned to the tall, grey-haired man just behind Ann and his mother he stepped forward, his own eyes moist. 'I'm Emile's father, Ann,' he said softly. 'And I'm very pleased to meet you—but you must be quite drained from the journey. Please, Arianne, let us take our guests into the house.' He turned to Sandi. 'And this must be Sandi? It was good of you to accompany your sister at this time; you must be a great comfort to her.'

Once in the house, the splendour of which rendered both women dumb, André and his wife were introduced—the former a smaller and plumper version of his handsome brother and his wife dark and pretty. Coffee was served by a small maid in uniform in the magnificent drawing room, the walls of which were hung with beautifully restored tapestries, but André and his wife declined to stay, returning to their own apartments once the introductions were over.

'You had a pleasant journey?' It was clear that Madame Challier was trying to act the perfect hostess, but her eyes were luminous with unshed tears as she looked at Ann and the atmosphere crackled with tension and embarrassment.

'Yes, thank you.' Ann put down her coffee-cup, clearly not knowing what to say. 'It was kind of you to ask us to stay...'

'I think it would be opportune to leave Maman and Ann alone for a few moments, Papa?' Jacques took charge of the situation again, his dark face autocratic. 'I will show Sandi a little of the house if you could organise Pierre into getting the cases from the car?'

'Of course, of course.' His father was patently glad of the opportunity to escape.

'But—' Before Sandi could object further she found herself whisked out of the room by a very firm arm at her elbow, and as Claude Challier disappeared to raise the said Pierre she turned to Jacques indignantly, her violet-blue eyes sparking.

'Ann's exhausted—she should be in bed. She needs—'

'She needs to talk with my mother.' The cool voice was inflexible. 'The first few minutes of a relationship are vitally important. You do not know this?'

'What I *know* is that you're the most overbearing man I've ever met,' she said tightly.

'This I do not consider a fault.' He leant against the wall, his eyes cool on her hot face. 'It is good for a man to know what he wants.'

'Is it, indeed?' She thought of the devastation Ian had caused in so many lives and her voice was bitter. 'You'll excuse me if I don't applaud that sentiment.'

'You know, Sandi Gosdon, for such a sophisticated woman of the world you have the most filthy temper,' he drawled lazily. 'You prefer your men to be little lapdogs, is that it?'

'I don't "prefer" anything,' she answered hotly. 'In fact—'

'In fact, it is not only Ann that is tired.' He uncoiled himself from the wall so swiftly that she was being ushered down the wide panelled hallway before she had time to think. 'You have been very brave for your sister, very protective of her rights, but now it is time for her to make up her own mind about this unfortunate state of affairs and you must let her.'

They had reached another set of ornate winding stairs, a replica of the ones which had faced her as she'd entered the house, but as he took her arm to lead her upwards she jerked away, her head turning backwards.

'I'll wait for Ann.'

'I think not.' The determined jawline hardened. 'My mother will not keep her long and then she will join you in the suite that has been prepared for your arrival and to which I am taking you now. She is your sister, Sandi, not your child, and very shortly she will have a child of her own to care for. It is time to cut the cord. You have your own life to lead.'

As she opened her mouth to fire back a hot reply he took all the breath from her body by whisking her into his arms and beginning to carry her up the stairs. 'I know, I know,' he said. 'I am this overbearing Frenchman that you cannot abide. This is sad, very sad, when I am sure we could have had fun together.'

'Put me down!' She didn't dare struggle in case they both toppled backwards. 'Now!'

'In a moment.' His voice was quite expressionless.

The sensation of being in his arms was fast taking all lucid thought from her head, his hard, lean body firm against her curves and the delicious smell that emanated from the dark, bronzed skin causing her head to whirl. She couldn't believe her body was reacting like this to a man she both despised and disliked. Even with Ian, at the height of her infatuation, she hadn't been in danger of losing control like this, and the knowledge was frightening.

'I said now,' she hissed angrily, risking one small struggle and then stiffening immediately as she glanced over his shoulder at the drop beneath them.

'And I said in a moment.' She turned her head to argue but it was a mistake. He had been waiting for the moment and capitalised on it immediately, his mouth hard and electric as it captured hers and his arms like bands of steel as they held her close. And then, almost immediately, his mouth was coaxing and warm against her lips, parting them as he penetrated the inner sweetness of her mouth and produced an exquisite torture that turned her fluid against him.

Her months with Ian told her that this was a man of vast experience, a connoisseur in the art of lovemaking, but even that knowledge was no defence against the wild response of her body. She wasn't aware that she had shut her eyes; she wasn't aware of anything except the feel of his body against hers and the drowning pleasure his lips were inducing. As he set her down at the top of the stairs against the wall some sanity returned, but then he leaned over her, both hands on the wall either side of her, as though he sensed her intention to escape, and his head came down again, his mouth searching.

'No...' She pushed against him but his answer was to move his long, hard body against hers, stopping all movement and creating sensations in her frame that made her legs tremble and her thighs hot. She knew she was returning the kiss, she also knew it was madness—but the force of her sudden desire, the demands of her body were too fierce to ignore.

His hands moved down her body in a light but passionate caress that made her flesh tingle under its layer of clothes and long for more direct contact, and her breasts swelled and ripened against his hard frame as her breath caught in tiny pants against his face.

'*Ma chérie...*' His groan of desire was soft and warm against her mouth, but somehow the fact that he hadn't said her name, that she had been regulated to the anonymity of '*ma chérie*', turned her to ice.

What was she doing? *What was she doing?*

The sudden twist she made to escape his arms took him totally by surprise, and in a second she was free. She knew what sort of a man he was. Emile had said that women couldn't keep their hands off him, so what was she doing playing with fire like this? Hadn't she learnt the hard way that men could go from woman to woman without it meaning a thing? And he had said himself that he thought they could have had 'fun' together—a brief affair, no doubt, where he would use her body until he tired of it and then move on to the next woman with no second thoughts, no regrets.

Like Ian. Just like Ian. Oh, she was such a fool, such a fool...

'Sandi?' As he went to reach for her she jerked back so violently that she hit the opposite wall.

'Don't touch me. Don't you dare touch me,' she ground out furiously. 'And keep your hands to yourself in future. I'm sure you think you're totally irresistible, but this is one female who is unimpressed by your undoubted talents.' Let him believe it, she prayed desperately as she spoke. Please don't let him guess how he's made me feel. Please...

'What the hell is this—?'

She waved her hand frantically as he made to move towards her again. 'I know your type, Jacques Challier—a woman for every occasion, is that right? I'm sure you can't even recall their names. Well, here's one that doesn't want to play.'

'Ah, I see.' He stared down at her, his eyes glittering with rage. '*Dans la nuit, tous les chats sont gris?* This is the way you suppose I think? The sort of man you assume I am?'

'What?' She had no idea what the French words, spoken with such biting contempt, meant.

'At night, all cats are grey,' he translated softly. 'You think I am a womaniser, a philanderer—the sort of man who is without morals, sensitivity?'

'Well, aren't you?' She was glad of the wall behind her; it was the only thing that was keeping her upright.

'Do not worry, Sandi.' He straightened suddenly and it was as though a veil had been drawn down over his face, masking all emotion. 'I have no intention of repeating what proved to be an interesting but all too easy experiment. I am male enough to appreciate something of a challenge in my love-life—you understand?'

The cruelty momentarily robbed her of speech, and then he was striding down the corridor in front of her, his words thrown over his shoulder through grim lips. 'This is the door to the suite which you and Ann will be sharing while you stay with my parents,' he said icily as he opened a door set in the long wall which was hung with ornate, expensive paintings and fine prints. 'It is quite self-contained and I trust you will find it comfortable.'

It took her a few seconds to find enough strength to follow him, but then she walked stiffly, her head up and her back straight. 'Thank you.' She walked past him into the luxuriously furnished room beyond. 'I'm sure it will be adequate.'

Adequate? The beautiful surroundings mocked such a meagre word with their magnificence, but she only had time to take in an enormous sitting room in blue and gold before she turned to face him again as he spoke.

'One of the maids, Charlette or Claire, will bring a cold supper once Ann has finished speaking with my mother. Breakfast is normally at eight here, but if you prefer to have it in bed just tell the maid when she brings the supper.'

'Thank you.' Go, go. For heaven's sake just go, will you? she screamed at him silently as she stared into the handsome face that was as cold as ice, his eyes glacial. She had made a terrible fool of herself; she hadn't needed him to spell it out in words. The way she had responded to him . . . She almost shook her head as the humiliation flowed through her, hot and fierce, but controlled the gesture just in time, although she knew her cheeks were burning. 'Goodnight.'

Once alone she put her hands to her hot cheeks and shut her eyes tightly, forcing back the stinging tears by sheer will-power. How could she have behaved like that? She didn't even like the man. He was arrogant, domineering and far too handsome for his own good, and if his ego was jumbo-size she had certainly done nothing to deflate it, had she, falling into his arms like an overripe peach?

She groaned out loud and forced her trembling legs to move as she got a tissue and blew her nose defiantly. Well, she wasn't going to crumble over this or any other stunt that Jacques Challier might pull. She'd come through far worse in the last three years and there was no way she was going to let him get under her skin— besides which she probably wouldn't have to see him again until she left France, if then.

She glanced round the elegant room slowly. She had a distinctly uneasy feeling that she would be leaving France alone, and if that was the case she would hire a taxi to the airport and fly back to England.

When Ann arrived at the suite a few minutes later it was clear that she had been crying but also clear that she was happier than Sandi had seen her since Emile's death.

'Your talk went well?' Sandi asked quietly as she left the unpacking in the big twin bedroom and walked through to the sitting room, where Ann had collapsed in one of the big easy chairs that were dotted about the room.

'Oh, Sandi...' Ann shook her head slowly. 'What that poor woman has gone through—and she's so full of remorse now about Emile's accident. She feels totally responsible, even not knowing the full circumstances.'

'So you're going to stay here until the baby's born,' Sandi stated flatly.

'I don't know... She wants me to.' Ann rose as easily as her bulk would allow and walked across to Sandi. 'Would you mind if I did? I think it's what Emile would have wanted.'

'Ann—' Sandi took her sister's hands in her own and looked full into the lovely face she knew so well. 'This is *your* life, *your* baby—you've got to do what you think best. It doesn't matter about me or anyone else; how do *you* feel?'

'I want to stay,' Ann said softly.

'Then stay.' Sandi smiled as she let go of her sister's hands.

'With your blessing?' Ann asked hesitantly.

'Of course with my blessing, you idiot!' Sandi hugged her close for a moment before she indicated the bedroom with a wave of her hand. 'Now, go and have a shower and get into your nightie; I understand our supper's arriving in a minute. And, in case I don't get the chance to mention it again, I shall expect to be informed once junior is on the way.'

'Of course.' Ann looked shocked.

'And you'll have to do some serious thinking over the next few days,' Sandi said quietly, 'about whether you want to keep the flat in England on or not. You can't just let things drift.'

'You'll stay here for a few days more?' Ann asked quickly. 'Like we'd arranged? Emile's mother wants to get to know you—she felt awful at the way Jacques bundled you off tonight.'

'He thought it was important that you two got to know each other.' Now, why had she said that? Sandi thought crossly. As though he needed defending! If there was anyone in the world who could look after himself it was Jacques Challier!

'Thanks for being so understanding, Sandi. I don't know what I'd have done without you the last few weeks,' Ann said huskily, her eyes misty. 'You've been such a support.'

'What else are big sisters for?' Sandi purposely kept her voice bright and her manner easy. One way or another there had been far too much emotion flying about tonight, and what Ann needed now was a meal and sleep. As did she!

She grimaced to herself when Ann had left the room and she was alone. She had never felt so emotional and exhausted in her life, not since— She shut her mind to all thoughts of Ian and marched into the bedroom to continue the unpacking, finishing both Ann's and her own just as Ann emerged from the large and very luxurious bathroom and the pretty little maid, Charlette, appeared with enough food to feed a small army.

Later that night, as she lay wide awake despite an exhaustion that was making her bones ache, her mind replayed the last scene with Jacques over and over again until she felt like screaming. This was ridiculous, absolutely ridiculous.

When the clock ticked to two o'clock she climbed quietly out of her bed and, after checking to make sure that Ann was fast asleep, padded onto the small balcony that led off the full-length windows in the sitting room. The night air was cool on her hot, troubled face and she breathed in its sweetness gratefully before curling up in one of the large cushioned cane chairs and letting the peace of the night steal over her taut nerves.

She would have given the world to go downstairs to
the kitchens and make herself a drink of hot milk, but,
apart from the fact that she didn't have a clue where
they were situated, the thought of wandering about the
huge château in the dead of night when she was a temporary guest, and a definite afterthought at that,
squashed the idea flat. She'd help herself to a drink of
mineral water from the small fridge in the sitting room
in a minute, she thought tiredly as she pulled the quilted
bedcover she had brought with her more closely round
her shape. Or maybe a long glass of orange... It was
her last coherent thought before sleep washed over her
in a thick blanket of warm oblivion.

'Sandi?' The soft feminine voice at her elbow brought
her out of a deep sleep, and as she opened dazed eyes
it was to stare straight into the concerned countenance
of Arianne Challier. 'You are unwell?'

'I—' She glanced round helplessly, realising as she
struggled to make sense of her surroundings that she
must have slept the night away curled up in the chair on
the balcony. 'I couldn't sleep. I came out here to sit a
while...'

'Is that all?' Relief made the dark brown eyes velvet-
soft at the same time as the early morning sunlight emphasised the lines running from the older woman's eyes
and mouth. It was a nice face, Sandi thought light-
headedly as she battled to come fully awake. Still unu-
sually attractive, but natural, warm...

'I'm sorry.' Sandi moved to sit up straight, wincing
as cramped muscles twinged in protest. 'I didn't mean
to fall asleep.'

'No, it is I who should apologise,' Jacques's mother
said quickly as she sat down facing her on one of the
other chairs. 'Normally the maid would bring the break-
fasts, but I wanted to do it today. I was worried when

your bed was empty and then I saw the curtains waving in the breeze from the open windows.'

They continued to talk for some minutes, and as they did so Sandi felt the most peculiar feeling stealing over her. She found herself warming to Arianne in a way she would never have dreamed possible this time yesterday, but at the same time she was conscious that she was fighting the emotion—frightened of it, even.

She didn't want to be drawn to this family, to this gentle mother-figure or her handsome, arrogant son. She wanted to be as the last three years had taught her it was wise to be—distant, aloof, remote, keeping herself separate from all sentiment, warmth and susceptibility, drawing her self-reliance round her like impenetrable armour to repel invaders. But these people were finding chinks in that armour.

She stood up suddenly, softening the action with a smile. 'You said something about breakfast?' she asked lightly.

'Oh, my goodness, yes.' Arianne jumped up quickly, her face stricken. 'I've left the trolley just inside the door. I do hope the food won't be cold now. There are warming dishes, but—'

'I'm sure it'll be fine.' Sandi found herself reassuring the older woman as if their roles were reversed, and caught herself up abruptly. There was something very endearing about Jacques's mother; she could see why he was so protective of her. 'Shall we go and see if Ann is awake?'

In the end the three women had breakfast together on the light-filled balcony that the sun was already warming with its mellow rays, and although there was the odd uncomfortable moment and awkward silence the meal went well. They were just finishing coffee when a knock sounded at the outer door. 'That will be Claire for the dishes,' Arianne said quietly, before she raised her voice to bid the maid enter.

However it wasn't the plump, pretty maid who stepped through the curtains a moment later but Jacques, devastating in black jeans and a grey silk shirt that revealed just enough of the broad, hair-roughened chest to make Sandi choke on her last mouthful of coffee.

'Good morning, ladies.' The black eyes roved mockingly over Sandi's pink face. 'I said I'd save Claire a job,' he said easily to his mother, 'and at the same time inform you that your presence is required in the kitchen regarding the menus.'

'*Oui, oui.*' Arianne touched her son's face in a little gesture of welcome as she rose. 'You slept well?' she asked softly.

Jacques nodded before glancing across at the breakfast table. 'Is there any coffee left?' he asked smoothly.

'No.' Sandi had answered a trifle too quickly, but the thought of sitting any longer in her dishevelled state, with only the doubtful comfort of the bedcover between her and those wicked black eyes, her nightie being wafer-thin, was too painful to contemplate. He, on the other hand, was as cool as a cucumber, his hair damp and slicked back from an early morning shower, freshly shaven and looking quite...quite... Her thought process faltered and died. What was he doing here anyway? she asked herself weakly. He had his own home. He'd *said* so.

'No problem.' His sardonic smile told her that he knew exactly what she was thinking, and the urge to hit him hard, kick him—*anything* to ruffle that overwhelmingly arrogant assurance—was so fierce she could taste it.

'I think you ought to leave Ann and Sandi to get dressed.' Arianne sounded a trifle shocked and Sandi blessed her for it. 'Jacques stayed here last night,' she added unnecessarily. 'I felt he had done quite enough driving for one day and that, knowing the road between here and his own home as well as he does, there was the possibility he might be...careless.'

'Not I.' Jacques hugged his mother close for a moment and Sandi knew he had seen—as she had—the shadow that had turned the brown eyes into pools of pain. The ghost of his brother straightened the hard mouth and wiped the mocking smile from his lips in an instant.

'And now you can come and make me some coffee,' he said firmly. 'The brew Claire served last night reminded me why it was necessary to find my own place. Why you have a housekeeper who arrives after breakfast and leaves at eight every night is beyond me.'

'You know Madame Jenet has worked for me for years,' his mother said placatingly as they left, after a nod at the two younger women. 'Did I tell you her daughter...?' As their voices dwindled away and the door closed behind them Ann turned to Sandi with a wry smile.

'He handles her very well,' Ann said thoughtfully.

'He loves her very much.' The way Jacques had distracted his mother from her pain had touched Sandi and she didn't like it; she didn't like it at all. He had so many facets to his personality, so many guises that she was beginning to feel quite bewildered. And she didn't like that either.

How soon could she leave? She pondered the thought as she showered and dressed, hardly aware of the wide-eyed, ethereal reflection in the mirror as she brushed her shoulder-length hair until it shone like liquid gold, fastening it high on her head in a cloud of curls. Ann would be fine here—she could see that now—so perhaps after one or two days, when she was completely settled?

Yes. She nodded to herself firmly. Two days at the most. She needed to get back to America, to her job, to the normality and routine it represented. She wanted to be safe.

She didn't dare question that thought when it materialised, a sixth sense deep in her subconscious warning her that it was best left alone.

CHAPTER FOUR

'I CAN picture Emile here, you know, Sandi—much more so than in England.' Ann was lying on one of the thickly upholstered sun loungers scattered round the wonderful pool under the shade of an enormous spreading copper beech. 'Don't you think that's strange?'

'Not really.' Sandi raised herself on one elbow as she stared back at her sister through dark sunglasses. 'He was very French, wasn't he?'

'Yes.' Ann turned her head away and silence reigned for a few moments before the sound of children's laughter broke into their solitude. Both sisters turned to look towards the far end of the massive pool, which was surrounded by trees and bushes, with just one entrance through which they had walked an hour or so earlier, and as they did so three small children ran hopping and skipping through the inlet, causing Sandi to leap to her feet, only to relax a moment or so later as they were followed by Jacques's tall, lazy figure.

'I thought they were going to fall into the water.' Sandi found that her hand was clutching at her throat and brought it sharply to her side. What was Jacques doing, letting those tiny children dash about near such potential danger anyway? She wasn't aware of the scowl on her face as the little group approached, but when Jacques was a few feet away she saw that a mocking, sardonic smile was twisting his mouth.

'You are going to frighten them to death with such ferocity.' He indicated the little trio at his side who had pressed into his legs, their small faces solemn now and their black eyes saucer-wide.

She glared at him for one more moment before forcing a smile to her face as she crouched down in front of the three little girls, aware that Ann had twisted onto her side and was viewing the proceedings with more interest than she had shown in anything that morning. 'Hello there, what are your names?'

'Bonjour. Comment allez-vous?' The eldest of the little mites, who couldn't have been more than four years old, spoke what was obviously a rehearsed welcome, but, not understanding a word of French, Sandi looked up helplessly at Jacques.

'She asked how you are.' He too crouched down at the children's side, his muscled brown thighs in their brief swimming trunks and broad, hair-roughened chest far too close for comfort now. 'They speak a little English—but only a little. They will learn more when they go to school.'

He spoke rapidly to the girls in their native tongue, which caused them all to grin at Sandi and then turn to Ann, their eyes wide again, and the eldest one repeated her little speech.

'Je vais très bien, merci. Et vous?' As Ann replied in their own language the three little tots took a step nearer, clearly intrigued. 'Emile taught me some basics.' Ann smiled at Jacques and Sandi before swinging her legs over the sun lounger and patting the empty space beside her, an invitation which the children were quick to take up, leaving Sandi and Jacques briefly crouched side by side in close proximity.

'You slept well?' As Sandi straightened he rose too, towering over her and causing a fluttering in her chest that she despised herself for.

Why did he have to walk round practically naked anyway? she thought testily. He was hardly decent! Those swimming trunks revealed more than they hid. And then she was astonished at herself for having noticed—well, more than *noticed*, she admitted grudgingly—exactly how his big frame was put together. And it was put together well. Very well.

A heat that had nothing to do with the beautiful weather brought the colour surging into her cheeks and she lowered her head quickly, letting her hair cloud about her face in a concealing veil.

'Fine, thank you.' She forced her voice into a cool tone that she was quite pleased with—until she glanced up again and saw the wicked sparkle in those deadly black eyes. 'The children? They are André's, I presume?' she asked coldly as she held the mocking gaze that seemed able to read her mind with no effort at all.

'You presume correctly.' He turned slightly and gestured to the three small girls who were giggling with Ann on the sun lounger. 'The smaller two, Anna-Marie and Suzanne, are twins, although not identical, and they are three years old. The elder one is Antoinette, who is a very precocious four-year-old, soon to be five. The other two girls, Ghislaine and Chantal, are at school, but you will meet them this evening, no doubt. I understand there was some resistance this morning to leaving the house before meeting their new aunts.'

Aunts? Now she did turn away, gazing out over the blue expanse of sparkling water. She made no reply. Aunt, *singular*, she thought. She had no intention of getting involved with this family, none at all.

'You have swum this morning?' The quiet tone fooled her and she turned to make a light rejoinder to find the dark brown eyes with their thick dark lashes tight and intent on her face.

'I—I—' She stuttered a little and heard herself with a wealth of contempt. 'No.' She took a deep, long, silent breath and tried again. 'No, I haven't. Ann and I forgot to bring costumes.'

'That is not a problem.' The deep voice was even, but as his gaze moved consideringly over her slight figure, which was clad in a brief suntop and long white skirt, her breathing was anything but. 'I do not think Odile's swimwear would fit you—five children in eight years of marriage has made her figure a little...rotund. But my mother has a host of costumes that would fit you. She, too, is slim and petite. I will arrange for some to be brought to your suite later.'

'No, no, it's all right, really. I shan't be here long—'

'You do not like the water?' he asked softly. Again that quiet tone deceived her, until she looked into the glittering black eyes that saw too much.

'Not particularly.' It was a lie, and as she shrugged gracefully she felt that he knew it. Exactly why she had lied about such an unimportant thing she wasn't sure, except that the need to ensure that this man learnt nothing about her, however insignificant it might be, was paramount. She had to protect herself from him. Her recognition of the fact wasn't reasoned knowledge but pure instinct, and all the more powerful because of it.

'That is sad. I feel a good swim is most satisfying— although there are other pleasures, of course, that more than equal it.' The tone was wickedly innocent and the look on his dark face more so, but before she could reply—if she could have replied with her composure shot to ribbons—he had gone on. 'Of course, with the pool in the grounds Odile and André have taught their children to swim from birth, and the girls are more at home in the water than out of it.'

He called the children by name then, and they immediately slid off the lounger and bounded to his side, divesting themselves of the short towelling robes they had on over their tiny black swimsuits and following him down the rounded sloping steps into the shallow water as they chattered like little magpies in rapid French. Within seconds the three tiny figures were shooting through the water in a way that left both Sandi and Ann open-mouthed.

'Well, would you look at that?' Ann smiled quietly. 'You needn't have worried about them falling in after all, Sandi. They're like little fish.'

'Mmm...' There was only one figure in the pool as far as she was concerned at that precise moment in time, and he was fascinating. The big, powerful, almost naked body was cutting through the water with such aggressive masculinity that it was literally making her toes curl, and although it made her furious with herself she was quite unable to tear her eyes away from his dark shape. A great wave of alarm swamped her as she realised she was positively ogling him. What *was* the matter with her?

She turned so suddenly that she almost lost her balance. 'I'm going back to the house for a moment; there's a book I meant to bring down.'

'Oh, right.' Ann was still sitting on the lounger with her eyes following the children, and the look on her face made Sandi hesitate before she left and give her sister a quick hug.

'All right?'

'Oh, Sandi, seeing those three has made me realise I've still got part of Emile with me.' There were tears in her sister's eyes, but Sandi heard a note of anticipation too. 'I'm so glad we came here.'

'It doesn't upset you? The fact that Jacques and André are so like him?' Sandi asked quietly.

'No. Perhaps it should do, but it doesn't,' Ann answered thoughtfully. 'In fact, I find it comforting.'

'Good.' Sandi hugged her once more before straightening. So she had been proved wrong and Jacques right about what was best for her sister, but she didn't mind—not after seeing Ann's face. Anything that gave her sister a modicum of peace at this time was fine by her. And Ann, with her placid, amenable nature, would fit perfectly into the Challier household—that much was becoming patently clear. As clear as the other indisputable fact that she, most certainly, would not. Not when Jacques Challier was around, anyway.

She took her time in returning to the pool and met Odile on the way back. She had gone down to fetch her children and was now returning with the three little girls, their dark curls damp and shining in the warm air. They talked for a few moments, Odile proving to be as warm and pleasant as her mother-in-law, and then Sandi continued down to the pool, where she found Ann fast asleep under the shade of the vast tree and Jacques, much to her annoyance, just pulling himself out of the water.

He'd done that on purpose, she thought waspily. Waited until she got back so that he could display that magnificent body to its best advantage, with the water gleaming on his dark skin like diamonds and the brief wet trunks leaving nothing to the imagination. It was just the sort of trick Ian had used, although she hadn't been aware of the calculated intent at the time. But she was now. Oh, yes, she was now.

'Stop frowning.'

'What?' Her mouth opened in a little O of surprise as he approached, before she had the sense to close it with a little snap.

'This ferocious expression that you adopt whenever I am in the vicinity,' he said mildly as he passed her and stretched himself out on a lounger in the full blaze of the sun just a stone's throw from hers. 'It is most unsociable.'

'Unsociable?' She was still standing to one side of her own lounger, which was only partly in the sun, and now moved it closer to Ann's as she glared at the inert figure a few feet away, her lips pursed tight.

'Unsociable.' He raised himself on one elbow to glance her way briefly, his eyebrows raised quizzically. 'There was no need to move. I wasn't going to bite.'

'I don't want to get sunburnt,' she said stiffly.

'How wise.' It was a mocking drawl as he lay back down again, his hands beneath the back of his head—which brought the broad male chest into muscled relief. 'But I would have thought a little attempt to bring some colour to that pale English skin would have been . . . practical?'

'Would you?' she asked with tight sarcasm. So he didn't like the colour of her skin, did he? Well, she really couldn't care less. She was burning with rage as she flopped down on the lounger, and once settled she lay stiffly for long minutes as she tried to force herself to relax. But it was no good. The motionless male figure to one side of her had her nerves twanging like guitar strings, and there was no way she could just pretend he wasn't there. He, on the other hand, seemed to have fallen asleep.

She glared at him angrily. Why was he here anyway? He'd told her he had his own home to go to. She could understand him staying the night after the long travelling hours of the day before, back across the Channel, but it was nearly midday now. She grimaced to herself at the unfairness of her thoughts. She really was getting this thing out of all proportion. He seemed to have the ability to turn her into something even she objected to.

'I have never known a woman who could twist her face into so many unpleasant expressions,' the dark voice drawled again, causing her to almost jump out of her skin. 'And such a beautiful face, too. You really have no appreciation of what God has given you.'

She met the black eyes without flinching even as her cheeks flooded with the colour he had lamented the lack of minutes earlier. 'But you, of course, fully appreciate everything God has given you,' she stated with bitter meaning. 'And no doubt use it to its fullest advantage.'

'Now, what exactly does that mean?' he asked lazily. 'I am sorry to be obtuse, but I'm not quite sure what

I'm being accused of here. You English have a way of making the most simple statement into an indictment.'

'I—' She stared at him helplessly, suddenly aware of the hole she had dug for herself. If she told him she thought he was flaunting his body for her benefit he would know that she was aware of him in a way she very definitely did *not* want him to know she was—but how else could she explain her cryptic statement?

'Yes?' He was clearly thoroughly enjoying her discomfiture, and she was just preparing to throw caution to the wind when the sound of his name being called brought his dark head jerking upright. She thought she heard him groan softly, but in the next instant he had risen to his feet and was walking swiftly to the entrance of the pool, where a tall, slim redhead had just appeared, closely followed by Arianne and another older woman.

There was a babble of French just as Ann stirred at the other side of her, opening dazed blue eyes slowly. 'Who is it . . . ?'

'Looks like Jacques has visitors,' Sandi murmured in a dry undertone as she glanced from Ann back to the effusive redhead, who had now draped herself round Jacques, her slim brown arms wound round his neck in such a way that the front of her body was pressed suggestively into his, her face uptilted for his kiss— which, Sandi noticed, was full on the lips.

As the party made their way towards them both girls rose from the sun beds, and Sandi had a brief impression of large brown eyes set in a heart-shaped face surrounded by a mass of wonderful red hair before she concentrated on Arianne as she made the necessary introductions.

'Ann, Sandi, I would like you to meet my dear friend, Simone Lemaire, and her daughter, Monique. Simone, Monique—my new daughter-in-law and her sister, Sandi.'

'How do you do?' As both girls murmured a greeting Simone stepped forward to embrace them in the traditional French fashion, kissing both cheeks as she held them to her.

'It is good that you have come.' It might have been her imagination, but Sandi felt that the remark had been addressed solely to Ann and that Simone's dark eyes had hardened briefly as she'd turned her head in her direction. The next moment Monique had followed her mother's example, and this time she knew for sure that her presence in the Challier household wasn't appreciated as deep brown eyes held hers for one split second, their depths as hard as jet-black coal.

'Simone and Monique are staying to lunch. Do you think it might be nice if Pierre arranged a barbecue by the pool?' Arianne asked Jacques as the six of them walked across to a table and chairs under the shade of a huge striped umbrella. 'It will be more relaxing for Ann. I'll get Charlette and Claire to serve drinks shortly.'

'You aren't working, Monique?' Jacques's voice was cool as he glanced at the redhead, who had positioned herself very firmly in the chair next to his.

'I've just returned from Bermuda.' Monique's voice fitted in with the whole package—sensual, rich and silky smooth, with the sort of sexy French accent most women would kill for. 'I'm quite exhausted, darling. I need lots of tender loving care.' Her eyes were hungry on his dark face.

'Monique is a model.' Arianne supplied the information helpfully. 'And really doing very well.'

'How interesting.' Sandi smiled, but there was no answering warmth in the beautiful face as Monique glanced her way. 'You get to travel often?'

'Too often.' Monique shrugged almost sulkily before her gaze slid from Sandi and fastened on Jacques's face, where it brightened considerably. 'I need to be home more.' There was no question about what she was insinuating, and Sandi found that she was keeping the smile in place through sheer will-power.

Talk about obvious! She met Ann's eyes for a moment and read both amusement and distaste in her sister's face at Monique's blatant statement of possession. So Jacques and Monique were an item, she thought silently as the conversation ebbed and flowed around her. It shouldn't surprise her. The other woman was exactly the sort of sensual, bold, beautiful female he would admire.

The fact that the knowledge bothered her hit her a second later, and almost instantly she dismissed it. Of course it didn't. Who he was involved with was none of her business—*none*. He could be sleeping with half of the country for all she cared, and probably had if what Emile had hinted about his brother was true.

'Sandi?' She suddenly became aware that the others had gone quiet and that everyone was looking at her.

'I'm sorry?' She smiled quickly, aware that the frown that Jacques had pointed out twice already was again in evidence. 'I was daydreaming, I'm afraid.'

'Monique asked you what your job entails,' Arianne said quietly. 'She has spent some time in the States and feels you must be very good at it to survive out there.'

'I don't know about that, but I enjoy my work anyway.' Sandi spoke directly to the young French-woman just as Claire and Charlette arrived with a trolley of drinks and crushed ice and took the others' attention. 'It's very hectic, though.'

'Yes, I can imagine this.' Monique slanted her dark eyes thoughtfully. 'You have a boyfriend? In America?'

'I have friends who happen to be male, but nothing of a personal nature.' She knew it wasn't what the redhead wanted to hear—those lovely eyes had flickered to Jacques even as she had voiced the question—but it was the truth. 'My work is all-consuming at the moment.'

'It is?' The finely shaped eyebrows rose just the merest fraction. 'So you are...how do they say?...fancy-free?'

She was persistent, Sandi thought grimly as she kept the smile in place. She had to give the Frenchwoman that at least. With a hide like a rhinoceros too—albeit an extremely beautiful rhinoceros. 'Yes.'

'Hmm...' Monique had been leaning forward slightly in her chair, Jacques having stood to help the maids with the drinks, and now she leant back, crossing her long, slim legs as her eyes narrowed still more. 'How long do you intend to stay here with your sister's in-laws?'

From anyone else it would have sounded, and probably have been, a perfectly legitimate enquiry, but coming from Monique's pursed red mouth it was a clear statement that she was in danger of outstaying her welcome, and Sandi recognised it as such. For a moment the carefully veiled rudeness had her lost for words, but the training she had received in the school of life over the last few years stood her in good stead, and she smiled coldly as she shrugged gracefully. 'I've no idea, Monique.'

She turned away as she spoke, signalling that the subtle questioning by the other woman was at an end, and as she did so she became aware that Jacques was looking down at them both, a dark frown on his face—although quite whom he was displeased with she wasn't sure.

'Monique.' He handed the redhead a glass of what looked like brandy and sparkling wine, and Sandi noted, with a little kick in her heart region, that he hadn't had to ask what drink she would prefer. He obviously knew her well, very well—but then she'd already worked that out with a little help from the lady in question, hadn't she? 'Sandi? What would you like?' As he turned to her, Claire hovering at his elbow, she looked directly at the maid as a sudden violent, and in the circumstances quite unreasonable, anger rendered her blazing mad.

'I'll have a glass of dry white wine, please, Claire.' The smile she gave the young girl was the best piece of acting she had ever done. It was as she'd thought—*just* as she'd thought. He was the type of man who enjoyed playing around, who liked women, most women, and that was fine. It was. It was just fine, she assured herself tightly. It didn't mean a thing to her. *He* didn't mean a thing to her, and—

'Here.' His fingers touched hers as he handed her the glass of wine Claire had poured, and she all but dropped it as the slight physical contact shot through her arm like a bolt of lightning.

'Thank you.' In direct contrast to her innermost self her voice was cool and contained as she turned away to speak to Ann at her side. She hated this man, this virile, blatantly aggressive male, who thought he only had to crook his little finger and women went down like ninepins. He was too handsome, too rich, too powerful and he knew it. Oh, yes, he knew it all right.

The barbecue continued well into the afternoon, Odile and the three younger children joining them just as they began to eat, which Sandi, at least, found a blessing. The three girls were little bundles of live wires, and Sandi found that by entertaining them she could keep herself slightly apart from the other adults without appearing rude.

The small children were delighted at her attempts to learn a few basic words of French, and there was much hilarity from the little corner by the pool they had moved to. By the middle of the afternoon, when Odile announced that they were to return to the house for their nap, the three tiny girls were totally won over, putting up quite a protest at the thought of having to leave their new friend.

'You are very good with children.' There was a note in Jacques's voice she couldn't quite place as he pulled out a chair for her when she returned to the table where the others were seated.

'They're fun,' she said lightly as his words brought the old twist to her heart that she had thought she'd had victory over. When she had married Ian she had dreamed of having his babies—several of them, if finances permitted—and when he had gone, and the dream had been so brutally smashed, the loss of those unborn children had been almost as hard to come to terms with as his betrayal and death.

'Fun?' Monique's voice was a mixture of laughing contempt and mockery. 'All those grubby little fingers and the oh, so shrill screams? You think this is fun?' She looked directly at Sandi as she spoke, and the extent of the other woman's antagonism, hidden from the others behind her smile but clear in the dark hardness of her eyes, paralysed Sandi's tongue for a moment.

'Oh, I love children.' Ann entered the conversation, her calm voice gentle and sweet as she placed her hand on Sandi's arm. 'Which is just as well, really.' She laughed quietly as she patted her swollen stomach meaningfully, at which point the conversation shifted to babies' names and everyone's preferences. But Monique was tenacious and the diversion only lasted a few minutes.

In a slight lull in the conversation the Frenchwoman surprised Sandi for the third time that day by turning to her, her voice clear and almost expressionless as she spoke. 'You did not consider a career with children, then? Caring for them like you do?'

Why her playing with Odile's children should have bothered Monique so much Sandi wasn't sure, but it was quite apparent that it had: the dark eyes were alive with dislike.

'Or perhaps the advertising world was more... lucrative?' Monique continued sweetly. 'Even though you have to be so tough to survive. I know how impossible it is to succeed as you have apparently done.'

On a scale of one to ten she would have to give her ten for sheer nerve, Sandi thought, with something akin to wonder tingeing her mind. With just a few well-chosen words Monique had implied, with perfect innocence, that she was both money-grabbing and ruthless—the sort of callous businesswoman who would make it to the top whoever she stepped over to do it.

'Yes, Monique would know this.' Even as Sandi opened her mouth to formulate some sort of a reply Jacques spoke. 'The modelling world is second to none for sheer heartless insensitivity. Is that not so, Monique?' He was smiling but there was something in his expression which Sandi couldn't quite place. 'Simone is very proud of the way her daughter has risen in such a competitive, dog-eat-dog environment.'

'Oh, I am. I am very proud of my little girl.' As Simone gushed on happily Jacques was still smiling, but whatever message he had endeavoured to convey to the young Frenchwoman had been understood; that was apparent in the set stiffness to her face, and her smile was tight and sharp.

The lunch party broke up just after that, when Simone mentioned an afternoon appointment and Ann decided that she was returning to the house for a lie-down. By unspoken mutual consent they all began to walk towards the entrance to the pool, beyond which stretched large bowling-green-smooth grounds with fountains and several small rose-entwined bowers of latticed wood—shady retreats from the heat of the sun—together with magnificent well-attended flowerbeds, perfumed and ablaze with colour under the blue sky.

Simone and Arianne were either side of Ann as they walked out of the pool area and as soon as they had risen Monique had taken Jacques's arm in a proprietorial gesture that reeked of ownership, her smile very much in evidence again when she flashed her eyes up at him as they walked. Sandi fell just a step or two behind as she followed the others out into the grounds.

'Sandi?' She wasn't quite sure if Monique let go of Jacques's arm or if he shrugged himself free of the Frenchwoman's grip, but in the next instant she found herself between them, Jacques's hand very firmly under her elbow. She blinked up into his face. 'You would like me to show you the grounds in a moment?'

'I—' She was vitally aware of Monique on her other side as something indefinable but definitely hostile communicated itself without words from the other woman. 'I— No—no, thank you. I think I'll go up with Ann and—'

'Nonsense.' The dark gaze swept over her face as it probed her mind. 'You have been resting all day and you are not with child; you have no excuse to be lazy. We will have a short walk before dinner, yes?' He gave her no chance to reply as his gaze moved from her slightly bemused face to Monique on the other side of her, the tall Frenchwoman almost on a level with his own considerable height. 'You drove your mother, Monique?'

'Yes.' The one word was curt and short, and then Monique underwent the lightning chameleon-type change that seemed an integral part of her make-up. 'Darling?' She had swung to Jacques's other side and taken his arm in one graceful movement, speaking softly in rapid French of which Sandi couldn't understand a word.

'English, please, Monique.' Jacques's deep voice was cool.

'A party. We are having a party this evening.' Monique glanced briefly at Sandi before her eyes returned to the man next to her. 'Nothing formal, just a celebration for my mother's birthday next week. You would like to come?'

It was quite clear that the invitation was meant exclusively for Jacques, and just as they reached the vast drive, on which was parked a small and very expensive red sports car, Simone turned round, overhearing what her daughter was saying.

'*Oui, oui.* Of course you must come, Jacques.' She smiled graciously. 'There are few people of Monique's age; it would be good if you came.'

'But of course we will come,' Jacques responded innocently as he turned to look down at Sandi by his side. 'It will be a chance to show you a little of the French countryside while you are here, yes?'

She knew that he knew she hadn't been included in the invitation, and she also knew, for whatever reason and in spite of his casual air and relaxed smile, that he was angry about it. Perhaps such unnecessary rudeness had grated on the excellent good manners which the Challier family had extended to their guests so far? Or maybe he just felt sorry for her? Whatever, she had no intention of going anywhere alone with Jacques Challier, and especially not to Monique's family home, where it would be very much a case of stepping into the lion's— or, to be more accurate, *lioness's*—den.

'I don't think—'

'Oh, do go, Sandi. It will do you good.' There were few times when Sandi wished her sister in another place, but this was one of them. 'You've been so wonderful to me over the last week or so and you need a break—you know you do—before you go back to America.'

'I'm having a break.' Sandi forced a smile that almost cracked her face. 'I'm thoroughly enjoying my time here—'

'And you will enjoy it all the more tonight.' There was a sardonic note in Jacques's voice that she didn't miss, and as her eyes rose to meet his she saw a definite challenge in the cool, shuttered gaze. He was *daring* her to go with him? The shock of it put fire in her eyes. He was. He was daring her to spend the evening with him.

'If Sandi doesn't want to come...' Monique allowed her voice to trail off with a faint trace of regret as she dropped her eyes, and that hypocrisy more than any-thing else brought quick words to Sandi's lips which she had never intended to say a minute before.

'I'd love to come, Monique,' she said brightly, tilting her blonde head in a little gesture of defiance that she was quite unaware of. 'If it's not inconvenient, of course.'

'No, no. As I said, the evening is informal.' The words were forced through lips that had suddenly set in a tight, hard line, and as Sandi glanced from Monique to Jacques she saw a small smile of satisfaction curve the well-shaped mouth for a moment.

What game was he playing? She glanced at him sus-piciously as Monique and her mother slid into the snazzy little car. Did he imagine he had two females fighting over the chance to be with him? Or was there some deeper meaning to all this? Perhaps a lovers' tiff with Monique? Something along those lines? And this was intended to bring the redhead to heel?

She found herself wishing with all her heart that she hadn't agreed to go, but when, in the next instant, Monique's brilliant red head popped out of the driver's window and she called out the time the party would start she didn't say that she had changed her mind. And as the little car roared off down the drive any opportunity to escape from an evening that was bound to be a dis-aster of unprecedented proportions went with it.

CHAPTER FIVE

'YOU look gorgeous, Sandi—absolutely gorgeous.' Ann breathed a sigh of satisfaction as she lay on her bed watching Sandi put the last touches to her discreet eye make-up. 'And please, just go and have a good time without worrying about me. I'm fine here.'

'You weren't fine earlier, when I came back before dinner,' Sandi accused her sister softly as she turned to look straight into her pale face. 'I always know when you've been crying.'

'I'm going to cry, aren't I?' Ann's voice didn't hold a trace of self-pity, rather a mature knowledge of her way of working through her grief that she hadn't expressed before. 'I loved Emile, Sandi, and I'll always love him. But that doesn't mean life has to stop for everyone else. I want you to go out tonight and have a wonderful time with Jacques—I mean it.'

A wonderful time? Sandi just stopped herself repeating the words in a tone that she knew would have been full of amazed contempt. She didn't expect to have a wonderful time; she expected— She expected something quite different, she told herself flatly as she shut off her mind from the route it was following. But thinking about it wouldn't help. She had to take the proverbial bull by the horns and get on with it. And the bull in question was at this moment in time waiting for her downstairs.

'You think this dress is OK, then?' she asked as she turned back to the mirror and had one last glance at her appearance. She had chosen a simple sleeveless dark wine-coloured dress in pure silk that she had bought a few weeks previously in America, the cut of which was exquisite. Quite why she had thrown it into her case at the last moment before leaving for England she wasn't sure—she hadn't been thinking straight at the time, after the distraught telephone call from Ann, who had been hysterical with shock and horror—but now she blessed the impulse.

She had fixed her hair into a high loose knot on the top of her head, allowing a few wispy golden curls to fall about her neck to soften the severe style, and had added a touch of violet-blue eyeshadow to her eyelids that emphasised the unusual hue of her eyes and the clear honey-coloured skin that surrounded them. Tiny stud earrings and high-heeled shoes in the exact shade of the dress completed her ensemble, and now, as she checked the wide-eyed reflection in the mirror, she was satisfied with the cool, worldly and remote image it presented.

And that was how she intended to be tonight, she told herself flatly. Cool, cosmopolitan and definitely—*definitely*—remote.

'Go on, go and wow them, Sandi.' Ann's smile was warm. It had been a long time since she'd seen her sister get ready for a date—over three years, in fact—and her soft mouth hardened as she thought of Ian Mortimer.

'I don't know about wowing them.' Sandi gave her sister a quick hug before straightening her shoulders as though she was preparing to do battle. And that was exactly how she felt, she told herself nervously. The tight tensing of her muscles, the rapid heartbeat and ridiculous flow of adrenalin were all down to the fact that she had been forced into a situation she both disliked and resented. That was all. There was no excitement mixed up in this feeling. *There was not.* And she was not attracted to Jacques Challier—in fact, he was everything she despised in a man.

He watched her every step as she came down the stairs, and Sandi had never found it so difficult to put one foot in front of the other. She purposely kept her eyes straight in front until she reached the foot of the winding staircase, when she turned and faced him for the first time, her eyes widening slightly as they met his, but otherwise her face concealing her thoughts from him.

He looked magnificent! She wanted to lick her suddenly dry lips as he moved towards her but forced herself to stand absolutely still and remain the ice-cool blonde. But he *did*, her brain told her with traitorous disregard for her thudding heart. She had never seen a man whose body carried an evening jacket the way this one did. His curly hair, as black as jet, had been persuaded into a more conservative style than normal and his skin could have been sculpted in bronze against the snowy white of his shirt, but the black eyes, as they held hers, were the same. Wicked, amused and mockingly aware of every thought in her head—or so it seemed to her feverish mind.

'You look very beautiful, Sandi.' His voice, with its sensual accent, was like liquid fire on her overwrought nerves, and she found herself blinking like a startled rabbit before she forced a light smile to her lips as her mind replayed the sight of him as he had been earlier, dripping wet and almost naked. She had to stop this— oh, she did, she told herself desperately. The only way to get through this evening was to match him in every way.

'Thank you.' She glanced at the small gold watch on her wrist as she spoke without raising her eyes. 'You look rather nice yourself.'

'"Rather nice"?' The tone of his voice brought her head up with a little snap, and as she had expected the dark eyes were alive with wicked amusement. 'That is very English, is it not? "Rather nice"?'

'I *am* English,' she said stiffly, and was further affronted when he laughed softly, his eyes lingering on the swell of her breasts through the thin material of the dress.

'But not as aloof and cucumber-cool as you would have me believe, I think,' he said softly. 'I have seen you with your sister, and a little tigress could not defend her young so admirably, and with the children this afternoon... You were not the cold English woman of the world with them.'

'Children are children.' She had wanted her voice to be mocking and light but it was merely breathless, and the slight tremble in its depths had her wanting to close her eyes with mortification.

'And what makes them different from the adult population in your eyes?' he asked quietly, all trace of derision gone now and his eyes deadly serious as they fastened on her flushed face. 'The fact that they are small, helpless? That you have no need to keep the formidable armour in place with them? Is that it?'

'Don't be ridiculous.'

His face hardened, a dark flare of anger in the midnight-black eyes as they held hers. 'I am never ridiculous.' It was said with such arrogance, such utter male authority that on any other occasion it would have brought a smile to her lips. But not now, and not with this man. 'You are hiding from life. I know it and you know it,' he stated coldly. 'Everything about you holds a subtle message that you are unattainable—'

'And that's why you wanted to take me out tonight?' she flashed back, with both pain and rage in her voice. 'Because you thought I was a challenge—'

'Partly.' He cut through the angry tirade with a cool smile as he spoke, her apparent lack of control restoring his perfectly. 'But only partly. I have to confess I find you intriguing, Miss Gosdon. I would like to know how someone so exquisite could have escaped the male jungle this long—how it is that some brave soul more cour-

ageous than the average man hasn't taken it upon himself
to put a gold band on the third finger of your left hand.'

'Someone did.' Her voice was utterly flat now, but
there was a wealth of pain in the violet-blue of her eyes
that stunned the man in front of her into total silence.
'And the brave soul is dead now. Shall we go?' So saying,
she walked past him and to the front door.

It was a good ten seconds before Jacques Challier
could bring himself to move, and even then it was quite
automatic, his mind on a different plane altogether.

'Sandi?' He caught her arm as they walked across to
the silver-coloured Ferrari crouching on the drive.
'Please, look at me.'

She turned because there was really nothing else she
could do, but her face was closed against the appeal in
his, her mouth tight and buttoned as she looked up into
his dark, handsome face.

'I had no idea. You believe this?'

'It doesn't matter.' She moved slightly, the gesture indicating to him to remove his hand from her arm. 'It all
happened three years ago. It's history now.'

History? Jacques Challier was suddenly filled with an
emotion he had never experienced in his life before, and
he had no way to describe it other than as a compilation
of burning curiosity, regret, dark anger and a hundred
other emotions besides raging through his frame. She
had been married? *Married?* And she still loved him even
though he was dead, if the look on her face was anything to go by. Why that should bother him in the way
it did he didn't know, but he did know that he didn't
like it, and the knowledge tightened his jaw and brought
a thread of harshness to his deep voice.

'Nevertheless, I had no wish to cause you pain,' he
said with a formal little nod of his head that was
very French. 'You accept my apology, Sandi?' His voice
was quiet now, quiet and low and very controlled, all emotion absent.

'Yes.' She answered automatically, and then her eyes rose to meet his.

The stillness of his body and the strange unfathomable expression on the hard male face momentarily pierced the shock and pain that his words had induced. If she hadn't known better she would almost have imagined there was something defensive about the posture of his body and tilt to his chin, but she was imagining it—she had to be—and when she blinked in the next instant the impression was gone.

'Yes, of course I do,' she said softly now as she forced her heartbeat to return to normal. 'Let's forget it, shall we?'

He nodded almost coldly before gesturing towards the car, and opened the door of the Ferrari without looking at her.

As she slid into the luxurious depths of the beautiful car she was aware that she was seeing a side to him she hadn't seen before. Earlier that evening, as they had strolled round the immaculately tended grounds before dinner, he had been the perfect host—courteous, attentive and very correct. She had expected— She didn't know what she had expected, she admitted to herself as he joined her in the car and the powerful engine purred into life, but it hadn't been the formal politeness he had shown at the time.

Ian would have capitalised on such an opportunity by making a subtle or maybe not so subtle attempt to make love to a woman, but Jacques Challier had returned her to the château with nothing more threatening than a cool, light hand at her elbow. And now? Now he was yet another person in addition to the dark, mocking philanderer he had appeared to be at the poolside—cold, reserved, with an almost visible aura of aloofness that sat on the big male body like a dark mantle.

They drove to the party in a silence that vibrated with electricity, and it wasn't until they were almost at the

Lemaire residence that Sandi relaxed enough to take in any of the beautiful scenery through which they had been travelling. Charming villages, gently dozing in the late evening air, and warm, rolling hillsides dotted with sweet-smelling orchards and vineyards were virtually at every bend in the winding road, and after they had passed one particularly impressive vineyard that seemed to stretch for miles she forced herself to break the silence that had reached screaming-pitch.

'I understand from Ann that the Challier family have been in the wine-making business for centuries,' she said quietly as she turned towards the dark profile at the side of her.

'This is correct.' The beautiful car, the lovely evening and the handsome dark man at her side were too intoxicating, she told herself tightly, leading her to all manner of foolish imaginings. She had to keep the conversation on a more mundane, ordinary level, like now. There was nothing at all mysterious about Jacques Challier. In fact, she could read him like an open book—like all his type. He liked women, plural—that much Emile had made clear—and he was involved with Monique—*that* much the tall, beautiful redhead had made clear. End of story.

'Your vineyards are close by?' she asked carefully.

'Yes.' He glanced at her for one brief moment and her heart thudded at the eye contact. 'I can arrange a visit before you leave if you wish?'

'That would be fun,' she said lightly. 'I'm sure Ann would be interested to see how things are done.'

'I'm sure she would,' he agreed drily, the lazy drawl in his deep voice telling her that he was aware of her intent not to be alone with him again and found it amusing. Well, that was fine, just fine, she told herself tightly. She didn't mind how the message got through as long as it was received.

Dusk had given way before the onset of a black velvet
night as they drew into the enormous drive of the
Lemaire château, but the moon washed the imposing
house with a bright silver glow as they drew to a halt in
a drive already jam-packed with similar cars. The wealth
of these people!

Sandi glanced round her as she stepped from the car
after Jacques had opened the door, and found Ian in
her mind again—much to her annoyance. These were
the sort of people he had craved in his search for wealth
and fun and high living. She shook her head slightly at
the thought, unaware of glittering black eyes watching
her every move.

'Something is the matter?' His voice was calm and
controlled, but there was a thread of something hard
and silky that brought her eyes snapping immediately to
his.

'No, no—of course not.'

'No?' He stepped back a pace, crossing his arms across
his hard-muscled chest as he surveyed her from cold,
dark eyes. 'I saw disapproval on your face—distaste
even. I was wrong in this?'

'I—' She didn't know what to say. Good grief, what
could she say? And then the temper this man seemed to
ignite with such little effort came to her rescue. 'I am
entitled to the privacy of my thoughts, surely?' she asked
with a coldness that matched his. 'And I hardly think
they would be of any interest to you.'

She had a warm, sensual mouth, whatever that ice-
cool-blonde image said to the contrary, he thought. He
stared at the full lower lip for one second more before
he crossed the yard or so separating them and took her
in his arms, his mouth taking hers in a hard, vital,
burning kiss before she even had time to realise what
was happening.

One hand was round her waist, the other at the nape
of her neck to give his searching mouth greater power

of invasion as he held her head at an angle that suited him. There wasn't a trace of hesitancy in the kiss, no suggestion of permission being sought, merely a bold taking of something he desired that took her completely by surprise and numbed all thought of resistance for a few incredible moments.

'No—' As her speech returned along with her senses she began to struggle, jerking her mouth from his, but even as he made a small gruff sound in his throat his lips claimed hers again, and he moulded her into his hard body in a way that made further resistance useless.

And then the kiss became one of sweet exploration, his tongue working with his hungry lips to send her senses reeling. This kiss was how she had always imagined a kiss could be—should be, she realised as her body made an instinctive arch into his. And her body was responding as it had done the night before when she had been in his arms—wantonly and without thought. But she *needed* to think.

This time when she struggled he let her go at once, moving her to arm's length with his hands dropping to her waist as he stared down into her flushed face.

'You said—' Her voice was shaky and she raised a trembling hand to her hair as she tried again. 'You said you wouldn't do that again.'

'I lied.' He smiled slowly, his dark eyes stroking across her golden hair before returning to her face. 'I am very bad.'

'I don't want—' She shook her head slightly as she searched for the rage that should have been there at his autocratic assumption that he could kiss her. 'I don't want this, Jacques—I mean it.'

'You do not want what?' he asked softly, his hands still refusing to release her. 'A kiss? You do not want a kiss? But what is so bad about that, little one?'

How could he change like this? she asked herself helplessly. During the drive here she had almost felt the dark waves emanating from the big male body at her side, and when they had first stepped out of the car he had been angry with her, she knew it. But now—now his mouth was curved in an attractive half-smile that caused the breath to constrict in her throat as she stared up at him, his broad, muscled shoulders and height dwarfing her slender, diminutive frame. Monique's tallness would suit him so much better.

The thought, coming from nowhere as it did, put iron in her backbone and gave her the strength to move away with a firmness that made his arms drop to his sides. 'There is nothing bad about it,' she said with a coolness she was far from feeling. Bad? it was glorious, wonderful and terribly, terribly dangerous. 'But I'm not into brief affairs or one-night stands, so if you don't mind—'

'One-night stands?' Well, she'd certainly got rid of the warm, ardent lover, she thought wryly as he metamorphosed in front of her eyes, his brows drawing together over glittering black eyes in an unholy frown as his mouth thinned and straightened. 'One-night stands?'

'Or whatever the equivalent is in France,' she said coolly as her stomach jerked and dipped like a roller coaster. 'Apart from the social sense it makes these days, I've always thought there should be more between a man and a woman than lust. Now, shall we go in to the party...?' Her voice trailed away when she saw the blackness in his face.

He stared at her for a full thirty seconds without speaking, and then took her hand in a tight grip that almost broke her fingers and practically ran her up the rest of the drive towards the huge steps fronting the massive studded oak door.

'What are you doing?' she asked breathlessly as she trotted along at his side, almost unable to keep her balance in the three-inch heels she was wearing.

'You want to go to the damn party?' he asked tightly. 'So we are going, yes?'

She arrived at the front door in a panting gallop, and was immeasurably glad that it was a few moments before their ring was answered as she endeavoured to bring her breathing under control. The pig. The arrogant pig! To manhandle her like that, just because she had objected to his lovemaking.

'And smile.'

'What?'

'*Smile!*' She had never heard anyone shout without raising their voice before, she thought weakly. 'There is no way I am walking through that door with you looking as though you are with the Marquis de Sade on a bad night,' he growled through gritted teeth.

As the door opened and a small maid ushered them into the baronial hall she found a smile from somewhere. It faltered for a moment as Monique appeared almost immediately from the edge of the throng of people in what looked like a vast drawing room. Her smile was radiant as she caught sight of Jacques, and her tall, slim body was encased in a black cocktail dress that made her slender legs endless and her red hair a mass of vibrant colour that was quite breathtaking.

'Darling...' She reached out slim arms in a gesture that should have looked theatrical—and would have done from anyone else—but which merely added to the Frenchwoman's charm. 'You're here. And Sandi...' When, in the next moment, Sandi found herself in a brief, highly perfumed embrace she forced herself not to show her surprise. 'It is so nice to see you again,' Monique said sweetly, her brown eyes wide and soft. 'You must come and meet everyone.'

And meet everyone she did. Simone was at her elbow the minute they entered the drawing room, slipping her arm through Sandi's and drawing her away from Jacques and Monique in a warm gush of words, then personally introducing her to every person in the place—which necessitated a great deal of smiling and nodding and desperate concentration to keep pace with the broken French accents.

After almost half an hour, with Simone's arm still tightly holding hers, Sandi was just thinking that she really couldn't smile again without her face setting in concrete when a dark voice at her elbow brought her head swinging round and up to meet Jacques's lazy smile.

'Introductions completed?' he asked Simone silkily.

'I think so.' Simone's eyes searched for Monique as she spoke.

'Then let me relieve you of your duties as hostess for this particular guest,' Jacques drawled smoothly, and drew Sandi into his side, taking the empty glass she had been holding as he spoke. 'Was that wine?'

'I— Yes.' She turned from him to smile her thanks at Simone, but the older woman was exchanging a glance with her daughter across the room, and as Sandi saw the almost imperceptible flick of Simone's head she followed her eyes to Monique's face.

They had engineered that, she realised with stunned surprise. Simone had deliberately kept at her side under the guise of hostess making a stranger welcome to give her daughter time with Jacques, and now she was calling her over. Simone surely didn't regard her as a threat to her daughter's relationship with Jacques, did she?

As she saw Monique begin to make her way over to them, Jacques's arm at her waist turned her round, drawing her out of the room and into the huge hall, where the sound of the music she had been hearing for the last ten minutes became louder.

'First a drink and then we dance, yes?' He guided her along the hall and into another vast room, one wall of which was lined with tables groaning with food and an army of waiters dancing attendance on yet more folk.

'I thought this was supposed to be a small, informal party?' she asked a trifle breathlessly as the touch of his hand burnt through the thin silk of her dress.

'It is. Believe me, by Lemaire standards it is,' he said softly. 'Monique and her mother are social animals of the first degree, and Philippe Lemaire indulges them both—it makes life simple,' he added cynically. 'You've met our host?'

'In the drawing room.' He had steered her over to a corner of the room where a large bar was being attended by four uniformed waiters as they'd spoken, and now requested a glass of dry white wine which was immediately placed in her hand.

'What did you think of him?'

'Think of him?' She stared up into the dark face as she took a sip of the chilled wine. 'He seemed nice. Friendly and warm,' she added quickly on seeing the flash of mocking amusement in his eyes at her choice of words.

'He is nice. He is also friendly and warm.' She began to simmer gently at the laughter in his face, but kept her face open and blank and her body still. She would not let him get to her. *She would not.* 'It is Philippe who is a friend of my parents rather than his wife. My father and Monique's father were boys together many years ago, and now the two families are closely linked with business ties.'

'Really.' How very convenient, she thought waspily. For Monique, that was. Not only did she have parental backing for her claim on Jacques but the two families' financial fortunes were entwined too. The tall redhead had had it handed to her on a plate, all things considered. She was surprised at how much the thought hurt.

'Come. We are going to dance.' He took the glass from her hand and placed it on a small table before pulling her with him out through the massive French doors at the end of the room and into the grounds of the château, which were lit as brightly as day. A small band was playing with both finesse and flair under a large striped marquee in one portion of the smooth green grounds that seemingly stretched for miles, and already the lawn was full of slowly moving couples dancing to a romantic ballad.

'I don't want—'

He put his finger on her lips as she protested. 'Come, come, little one, there must be some things you enjoy,' he said silkily. 'You do not swim, you do not dance—'

'I didn't say I didn't dance,' she shot back quickly, incensed at the mockery.

'But you don't want to dance with me.' Now all laughter and amusement were wiped clean from the dark male face and his eyes held hers in a penetrating grip she couldn't break. 'As you did not want to swim with me.'

'Jacques—'

'No, no, Sandi.' As he drew her against him she knew that he was perfectly controlled and absolutely determined to have his own way. 'You will dance with me. I want to hold you in my arms, and as you have made it perfectly clear this is the only opportunity I shall have for such pleasure I intend to make the most of it.'

'You're a pig,' she said weakly.

'Not the most inspiring of phrases for such an occasion, but for the lack of anything else it will have to do.'

This was a game to him, just an amusing game, she thought helplessly as he drew her against him, holding her so close against his broad chest that of their own volition her hands crept up to entwine round his neck as they danced. She was aware of the waves of pleasure moving from her head to her toes as she drank in the smell and feel of him but she fought them—desperately.

She had been here before, only once before in her life, and look where that particular road had led—straight into hell. She had never thought she would surface from the despair and black pain that Ian had plunged her into but she had—admittedly by the skin of her teeth, but nevertheless she had clawed back a life for herself and had learnt to live again, on her terms. And they didn't include flirting with a tall, dark, handsome man of the world who was already involved with at least one woman that she knew of and possibly several more. It was emotional suicide. And she didn't have a death-wish. Not any more.

'Stop fighting me, Sandi.' The shock of hearing him read her mind brought her head back, and as she looked into his face he kissed her full on the lips, but lightly this time, his mouth stroking hers with a warm, thrilling caress before he raised his head.

'I'm not.' The protest was weak and she knew it.

'No?' The sardonic voice and dark brows raised in mocking disbelief made her want to kick him—hard. 'However much you try to disguise your femininity from me you can't hide it from yourself, you know. You are attracted to me. I know it and you know it, although you don't want to admit it yet.'

'How dare you?'

'Oh, I dare much more than this, little one,' he drawled silkily as his eyes gleamed darkly. 'Your husband has been dead three years, is this so?' The shock of his words brought her jerking way from his body but the strong, steel-clad arms didn't relax their hold for a moment. 'Is it?'

'This is nothing to do with you—'

'And if I read all the signs correctly you have in effect been on top of the funeral pyre all that time.' It was cruel, he knew it was cruel, but it was the only way to get through that iron reserve that was holding him at bay. And he wanted to get through it—badly. The feel of her body next to his was affecting him in a way he couldn't believe. When had he been hit by such raw desire before? Not in a long time—a long, long time. 'Burying yourself in your work, holding everyone at bay as you carve a career for yourself—'

'There is nothing wrong in having a career.'

'There is if the personal cost means that you become isolated, a robot—'

'You know nothing about me,' she said hotly, her cheeks scarlet. 'Nothing.'

'Something I would like to remedy,' he said softly.

'You're talking about sex.' She spat the words at him, her face and body taut. 'That's all. Just a bodily satisfaction.'

'Am I?' He considered her through half-closed eyes for a moment before pulling her close against him again, his muscled strength too hard to withstand. 'You think this is all? Of course the physical aspect of a relationship is important—'

'How many women have you had, Jacques?' He had been blunt—well, so could she be, she thought angrily. 'How many?'

'What?' She wasn't to know that she had done what most people would have considered impossible—surprised Jacques Challier twice in one evening—but nevertheless she did get a measure of satisfaction from the amazed glitter in his eyes.

'You heard what I said. I asked you how many women you have had in your life—liaisons, affairs, call them what you will,' she said with brittle control. 'I want to know.'

'Zut!' The oath was short and sharp as the smooth control faltered for a moment, but then, as he caught the disapproving glance of a portly matron at one side of them, he breathed harshly before tilting his head to look deep into her eyes again. 'More than I would like at this moment in time.' The honesty surprised her and she remained silent as he stared down at her. 'But I am a grown man of thirty-six, Sandi, and I am no saint. I

have never pretended to be. I would say in my defence that I have lived my life by my own rules and never knowingly taken what was not mine to take.'

'And that makes it all right?' she asked flatly.

'As far as I am concerned, yes.' He eyed her darkly. 'And now I will ask you something. From the moment we met you have made it clear that you dislike me. You are attracted to me—' he raised his hand to her lips when she would have interrupted '—but you dislike me. This is a fact. Now I think I deserve to know why.

'It cannot be Ann any longer; you have seen yourself that she is welcome, more than welcome, and loved by my family. I expected this... antagonism to diminish when Ann made her decision to stay but it has increased—with me, that is. I could suppose that you are sulking at being proved wrong, but you are too strong a character for such petulance.'

She should have been pleased at the veiled compliment, but strangely she wasn't. In fact, at that moment her whole self was taken up with the fight not to burst into tears. She hadn't wanted this—she hadn't wanted any of it, she thought wildly. She had flown to England just over two weeks ago with one thought in her head and that had been to comfort Ann. The Challier family, Jacques, they had forced all this on her, and she wasn't ready to handle it—not any of it—and especially not Jacques.

Her life was settled now, orderly, in control, and although she wasn't exactly happy she had regained her peace of mind—which meant the world to her after losing it for so long after Ian. If she had thought about the future at all it had been with regard to her work, not her love-life. In fact she didn't want a love-life—not ever. The old adage of once bitten, twice shy still held good in this day and age, and especially with a man like Jacques, who was already deeply involved with another woman and had made no effort to pretend otherwise.

Some women could handle casual affairs, relationships that asked for nothing more than a little fun and excitement, but she wasn't one of them. She never had been, even before Ian.

'All right, all right, we will talk later.' The expression on her face caused him to move her close to him without another word as they continued to dance to the music, and, although she was glad of the respite from those piercing dark eyes that saw far too much, his closeness was having a dire effect on her metabolism.

What was it with her? she asked herself angrily as the warm heat in her lower stomach transferred itself to different parts of her body. It was as though she had a self-destruct button that fired with a certain type of man—the Ian Mortimer, Jacques Challier type. She had heard of women who were attracted time and time again to real swines, but until now hadn't put herself into that category.

'You are enjoying the party, Sandi?' As the deep-throated, sexy, feminine voice sounded just over her left shoulder she shut her eyes tightly for a second, before lifting her head and turning to face Monique and her partner.

'Very much, thank you,' she said politely as Jacques's arm slid to her waist and they surveyed the other couple. Monique's partner was a tall, good-looking young man with dark brown hair and deep blue eyes and the sort of physique that suggested a great deal of weight-training.

'Let me introduce Jean-Pierre,' Monique continued sweetly as she placed a red-taloned hand lightly on the other man's arm. 'He works with me.'

'You're a model too?' Sandi asked when the brief introductions were over.

'No, no.' Jean-Pierre laughed as he grimaced disarmingly. 'Me, I could not stand all the pirouettes and panics if I got a spot on my nose, you know?' Sandi couldn't see the suave, impeccably dressed individual in front of her ever having something so mundane as a spot on his nose, but she nodded anyway. 'I photograph—you know—click-click?' He made a little gesture as though he had a camera in his hands. 'This suits me.'

'And he's excellent at it, aren't you, Jean-Pierre?' Monique was at her most gushing. 'In spite of some of the...how shall I say?...bimbos you have to work with.'

'That is naughty.' Jean-Pierre shook his head at her before turning back to Sandi. 'She is a bad girl, this one.' Oh, she believed it, Sandi thought wryly. She really didn't need to be convinced.

'You would like to dance with me, Jacques?' Even as she spoke Monique took Jacques's arm and dimpled up into his face. 'Jean-Pierre will look after Sandi—won't you, darling?'

'Of course; it would be a pleasure.' The young Frenchman looked as though he meant what he said, and Jacques surveyed him through cool, shuttered eyes for a long moment before he allowed himself to turn and take Monique in his arms as the music began again. 'You would like to dance, Sandi? Or maybe something to eat and a drink?'

Jean-Pierre was a little smaller than Jacques, she noted as he smiled down at her, but there was something open and engaging about the young man's face that she liked. And as they danced she found that her first impression had been right, for Jean-Pierre proved both an amusing and very natural companion, his rather caustic wit and quite wicked sense of the ridiculous making her laugh more than once as they circled the lawn.

She didn't glance to left or right, keeping her eyes very firmly on the handsome face in front of her. Somehow the prospect of seeing Monique in Jacques's arms was to be avoided at all costs. But it was Jean-Pierre who forced the issue some minutes later.

'They make a handsome couple, do they not?' When he inclined his head to the side she followed the gesture without thinking, and then found that her stomach seemed to have risen up into her throat as she caught sight of Monique draped all over Jacques as they danced. 'Whenever I see them together like this I am always surprised Monique does not quit the rat race of modelling and concentrate on the Challier fortune instead.' His tone was slightly astringent.

'You see them together often?' Her voice was as light as she could make it, and it seemed to satisfy Jean-Pierre because he didn't even glance her way as he kept his eyes on the beautiful redhead.

'Now and again, at social functions like this one,' he said absently. 'You will find the beautiful people's set is quite a small one. The cost of the entrance fee is too high for mere mortals.'

'You're here.' She hadn't meant it quite as it had sounded, but now the vivid blue eyes did snap back to her face for a startled moment before he burst out laughing, throwing back his head as he let out a delighted bellow that brought more than one head turning in their direction—and in particular a pair of dark, glittering black eyes.

'This is true. This is very true.' He laughed again as he looked down into her lovely face. 'But I am something of a cheat, you know? It just so happens my father has an inordinate amount of money—which is very bad taste to mention, incidentally, but true nevertheless.'

'So you're one of the beautiful people too?' she asked with a wry smile.

'So it would seem.' His eyes moved back to Monique. 'But not beautiful enough.' He spoke the words almost to himself before his gaze snapped back to her watchful face. 'But enough of this. I am sure you would like a drink now, yes? And perhaps something to eat?'

'Yes, please.' The brief revelation that Jean-Pierre was head over heels in love with Monique further dampened her spirits as she walked hand in hand with him to the edge of the lawn. There he found two seats before disappearing, only to return a couple of minutes later with a small tray containing two plates of food and two glasses of chilled white wine.

The knowledge of how Jean-Pierre felt about Monique somehow strengthened Monique and Jacques's relationship, although she couldn't quite explain how. Did they see other people as well as each other? she thought flatly as she sipped at the expensive and delicious wine. Perhaps it was one of those modern affairs where they both indulged in any sexual flirtations they felt like when they were apart, knowing that what they had would stand such behaviour? She gave a mental shake of her head. She knew there were people who could cope with such relationships but she didn't understand them.

'You look sad.' As Jean-Pierre spoke at her side she smiled up at him quickly and shook her head.

'No, no—of course I'm not. How could I be when I'm in such good company?' He bowed at the compliment and his eyes laughed at her.

'Not too bad for one of you reserved English, I think,' he teased smilingly, spearing a large juicy prawn from his plate and offering it to her as she smiled back at him.

She really did like him, she decided suddenly, and the knowledge that he was in love with Monique and was asking nothing more of her, Sandi, than a little light amity and conviviality made her relax with him in a way she could never have done with Jacques, her face open and warm as she laughed with him when the prawn slipped off the fork, narrowly missing her cleavage to land with a plop on her plate.

'It must be a good joke to make you laugh like that.' The dark voice was like a heavy douche of ice-cold water, and the plate almost jerked off her lap as she jumped and then raised her eyes to see Jacques and Monique at their side.

'Not really.' Jean-Pierre rose swiftly, offering his seat to Monique. 'Can I get you some food?' he asked the lovely redhead after one lightning glance at Jacques's tight face.

'Thank you, darling.' Monique sounded sulky, and the next few minutes until Jean-Pierre returned with Monique's plate were spent in an uncomfortable silence which Sandi couldn't break for the life of her. She nibbled at the food on her plate with her eyes downcast and her thoughts in turmoil. How dared he object to her laughing with Jean-Pierre when he had been doing goodness knows what with his mistress? How dared he?

Almost in the same instant that Jean-Pierre returned with the food she found herself lifted to her feet with a firm hand under her elbow. 'A most enjoyable evening, Monique...' Jacques's voice was cool and contained and controlled.

'You are leaving? But it is so early—'

Jacques cut into Jean-Pierre's remonstrance with a smile that would have chilled ice. 'Nevertheless, it is time that we said our goodbyes,' he said grimly. 'You will thank your mother for us, Monique?'

It was noticeable that the lovely Frenchwoman barely raised her head as they left, and also that Jean-Pierre's expression held something of surprise and awareness in its depths as he bent over her hand in a continental gesture of farewell. In the next moment, Jacques whisked her along towards the house and through the noisy throng filling the downstairs rooms with laughter and chatter, and she barely had time to catch her breath before they were out of the front door and into the relative quiet of the enormous drive.

'Is anything wrong?' She shook his hand off her elbow as he prepared to lead her down the steps, refusing to be intimidated for a second longer.

'Wrong?' He paused for a moment two steps below her to look into her face, his voice cold and civilised. 'What could be wrong, *ma chérie*?'

'I don't know, but you seem ... annoyed at something,' she said a trifle breathlessly. Standing as he was on the lower steps, his head was just above her but almost on a level, and she found the nearness of his hard, firm mouth disturbing, her eyes leaving the thin, well-shaped lips with difficulty to fasten on the glittering black eyes that were looking directly into hers.

'I do?' His smile held no warmth. 'Then this is a puzzlement to us both. Now, shall we?' As he gestured to the Ferrari some way down the drive the motion of his hand was sharp and fierce, and she knew, she just knew that he was holding onto that iron self-control with an effort.

But why? What had bothered him? Had he had some sort of a row with Monique? Perhaps she had voiced her objections to her lover bringing another woman to the party—even though he had merely been fulfilling the obligation that had been virtually foisted on him by the fact that Monique had mentioned the party in front of her in the first place. The Challier family were excellent hosts, she would give them that, and, looking back, she could see that it would have been the height of rudeness on Jacques's part not to include her in his reply. He probably hadn't really expected her to come at all.

When she still didn't move he gave her one last long glance of grim exasperation before turning and walking down the drive towards the car, and as she followed, her footsteps quiet and slow, she suddenly felt that she had never been so miserable and alone in all her life.

CHAPTER SIX

'JACQUES?' The grim profile was not exactly encouraging, but Sandi felt she had to voice the suspicion that had been growing in her mind for the last twenty minutes or so. 'I didn't think the journey here was this long.'

'It wasn't.'

'But I don't understand—' She stopped abruptly as he swung off the main road on which they had been travelling for almost three quarters of an hour and onto a dark, wide lane that was bordered on both sides by the outlines of huge leafy trees. 'Where are we? Where are we going?'

'We are exactly two miles from my home—which is also our destination,' he said coolly, with a low silkiness that told her he knew exactly how his words were going to be received.

'Your home?' He didn't need to wince to tell her how shrill her voice was, and she didn't care. She couldn't believe this. She just couldn't believe it. 'You're taking me to your home?' she asked furiously. 'Without even telling me—asking me?'

'Which would you have preferred?' he asked frostily. 'To be told or to be asked?'

'You can turn this car round right now.' She glared at the implacable profile when he made no reply. 'Did you hear me, Jacques? I want to go back.'

'Of course you do, and so you will...later.' He turned to smile at her for one brief moment, his face a dark bronze in the night and his teeth flashing white. 'I only want to show you my home, Sandi—this is no crime, surely? I was finding the party a little...boring, but the

102

night is still young. We will worry my parents if we return so soon. They will think we have had a disagreement.' The last words were said with a mocking note of irony that was not lost on her.

'I don't care what they think,' she grated furiously. 'I want to go back.'

'Don't be tedious.' His voice was lazy now, with a shred of amusement that told her he was thoroughly enjoying her reaction. 'I will show you my home, we will have a quiet cup of coffee like two civilised people and perhaps even talk to each other without fighting.' He glanced again at her angry face and sighed loudly. 'Or maybe the last part is too ambitious?'

'You had no right to bring me here without asking first,' she said tightly. 'No right at all.'

'I know.' The admission brought her head swinging round, and she saw to her immense irritation that he was smiling. 'But if I had asked you to accompany me to my home this evening we both know exactly how you would have replied.' He quirked his eyebrows sardonically. 'Do we not?'

'You're impossible.' It was a *fait accompli*, and there was nothing she could do but try and get out of this with a little dignity.

'I know that too.' And there was a satisfaction in the sensual French voice that made her want to hit him with concentrated force in the place where it would hurt most. As it was, and mainly due to the fact that the Ferrari was travelling at a speed well over seventy miles per hour on an unlit road in the middle of the night, she contented herself with a loud 'huh', an icy lifting of her head and a tight stiffening of her body.

Within a few minutes the road narrowed to little more than a dirt track, and then they were passing through wide-open wrought-iron gates into a large courtyard, complete with duckpond and resident ducks, which was

lit up as brightly as day as soon as the car approached
the building in front of them.

'My home.' Jacques brought the car to a halt in front
of a large, sprawling thatched-roof farmhouse of mellow,
honey-coloured stone that was partly covered with sweet-
smelling roses and trailing ivy. Diamond-leaded windows
and dark wood doors completed the air of timelessness
about the place, and on the top storey the windows
peeped from the overhanging thatch, with tiny balconies
filled with a profusion of scarlet and mauve
bougainvillea.

'Oh, it's lovely. It's really lovely.' She turned to him
impulsively as the sound of the engine died away. 'What
a wonderful place to live.'

'Yes, it is.' The dark eyes were watching her intently
even as his mouth curved in a warm smile at her sincere
praise of his home. 'Not exactly on the lines of the
château but I like it.'

'Oh, it's much nicer than the château.' She spoke
without thinking, only to blush a deep red as she realised
what she had just said. 'Not that your parents' home
isn't beautiful, of course—it is—but this is more homely.
I mean—'

'I know what you mean.' He interrupted her rush of
embarrassed words with a nod and a reproving finger
on her lips. 'And I agree, utterly. Now, come and see
inside.'

A few geese waddled across to their side, cackling a
protest at having their slumber interrupted, but they were
all bark and no bite, and although Sandi gave a little
squeal at their approach they merely surveyed her
through bright black eyes before gathering together again
like noisy, gossiping old women. 'Ducks and geese?' she
asked Jacques as they walked across to the old studded
wooden door.

'They came with the place originally and then I found
I liked having them around,' he said quietly. 'My lifestyle

is not conducive to pets of any kind—sometimes I don't
return home for days at a time—but they survive quite
happily with the pond and the food I leave for them. I
have a lady from the village a couple of miles away who
comes in twice a week to clean and so on, but otherwise
I fend for myself.'

'I see.' She didn't ask if it was business or pleasure
that took him away from home so often; she didn't want
to think what his answer might be.

She had somehow sensed what the interior of the
farmhouse would look like, and she wasn't disappointed
as her eyes took in the plain whitewashed walls filled
with fine paintings, the beamed ceilings, the thick dull-
rose-coloured carpet that stretched through all the
downstairs rooms and the dark wood antique furniture.
The kitchen was huge and beautifully restored in a way
that kept its olde-worlde feel at the same time as providing all mod cons—even down to a large dishwasher
hidden behind carved wooden doors.

Everything seemed to blend together into a perfect
whole, accentuating the initial impression of quiet repose
and serenity that the exterior of the house had given.
She found that it disturbed her that Jacques had chosen
such a place for his home. She would have preferred to
find him living in a brash, modern bachelor pad or a
luxurious apartment close to the city's nightlife, not in
this peaceful old farmhouse with its air of tranquillity.
And the fact that she was thinking such thoughts disturbed her even more. It was nothing to her where he
lived—of course it wasn't. *He* was nothing to her.

'You are frowning again.'

'What?' She came out of her reverie to find him
standing in the middle of the wide square hall, from
which a twisting flight of stairs led upstairs, with his
eyes tight on her face.

'You are frowning again,' he repeated grimly. 'I was
going to ask you if you would like to see the bedrooms,

but with such a fierce expression on your face perhaps
that would not be a good idea?'

'I'm not frowning.' The protest was weak and they
both knew it. 'Your home is lovely—enchanting—and I
would like to see upstairs, if it isn't too much trouble.'

'What has displeased you?' He didn't move as she
walked slowly to the foot of the stairs.

'Nothing—I told you.' She turned and faced him,
keeping her voice bright and her face smiling.

'This home of mine does not fit in with what you expected of me?' he asked, with the devastating intuitiveness he had displayed more than once. 'You expected
something less...harmonious?'

'Not at all.' She had never found it easy to lie deliberately, and it was all the more difficult with those
piercing black eyes holding hers.

'I do not think you are telling the truth but, as you
reminded me on another occasion, your thoughts are
your own.' His voice was deep and quiet, and as he
moved over to where she stood his hands went round
her waist and he looked down at her. 'For such a tiny
little thing you have a heart and mind of iron, do you
not?'

'No—'

'But yes.' As she tried to slide out of his grasp his
hands tightened. 'Iron.' His eyes were half-closed as he
surveyed her, dark and gleaming in his tanned skin.
'When I first saw you at the door of Ann's flat I thought
you were a fragile little slip of a girl—young and
curiously innocent in spite of being, as I thought, my
brother's wife. And then...then I learn you are the sister,
the older sister, who is a force to be reckoned with in
the advertising world, fierce and ambitious—'

'Jacques—' He ignored her interruption as though she
had not spoken, his voice still low and deep but with an
inflexion that made her weak.

'A career woman, hard and uncaring. But almost immediately that illusion is dispelled as the tigress defends her young—or in this case her sibling—and I learn that you sacrificed much for your sister when your parents died, at a time when no one would have blamed you for carrying on with your education, for putting yourself first.'

'Look, this is all history—shall we go upstairs? I mean... You—you were going to show me the rest of your home,' Sandi stammered weakly as the nearness of him began to do crazy things to her shaky composure.

'And then I see the ice maiden as you come with me to my parents' home—the cool English blonde who is disdainful and haughty and proud—'

'Jacques, *please*—'

'And just when I think I have made a mistake, that you are really as cold and remote as you wish me to think, I learn you have been married—married and widowed—that you have loved a man and agreed to commit your life to him—'

'*Jacques!*' Now she did jerk out of his hold, her face fiery.

'And at that moment I see another side of this slender, tiny will-o'-the-wisp who has exploded like a meteor into my life. A passionate, fiery, fierce side—but a side that is full of pain—'

'I don't want to continue this conversation, Jacques.' And now her voice did stop him and she stared, trembling and white, into his face. 'I will not discuss this with you.'

'And Jean-Pierre? Is he the type of man you would discuss such things with?' he asked tautly.

'Jean-Pierre?' For a second she didn't recognise the name, so completely had she forgotten the other man.

'That was still another Sandi, there in front of me tonight,' he said tightly. 'You laughed with him, looked at him in a way—' He stopped abruptly, taking a deep, hard breath before he spoke again. 'In a way I had not seen before.'

It hadn't been what he had intended to say, she felt sure, but she didn't pursue it.

'He was amusing, that's all.' She couldn't quite believe she was having this conversation. In the last three years she had made it her business to keep the male population very firmly at arm's length, and now somehow she was in the home of a man she had only met a few days ago, it was the middle of the night, and, worse, he expected her to bare her soul to him!

Panic hit her like a hard punch in the chest. It was obvious that she represented something of a challenge to him—that much he had made plain himself—but it was also crystal-clear that any lowering of her guard would result in a brief, no doubt torrid affair that he would be able to dismiss as easily as he would dismiss her when the time came for her to leave. He would return to Monique's eager arms and she—she would be crushed, devastated.

But that wouldn't happen; of course it wouldn't, she told herself as she surfaced from the mindless darkness that had briefly taken hold of her. Because she wouldn't let it happen. It was up to her. Most men would take what was on offer, so she wouldn't offer. It was as simple as that.

'Sandi—'

'You brought me here to show me your home.' Now she didn't have to engineer the coldness in her voice. 'So show me.'

He straightened as she spoke, reached across the space separating them and took her in his arms, kissing her fiercely and angrily and without restraint. And, like before, despite her fears and panic, her alarm at the thought of where it might lead, she couldn't help kissing him back. She wasn't sure what happened to her when he touched her—this mindless yearning that sprang up from the very depths of her hadn't been there even with Ian—but it was strong and potent and so sweet that she had no defence against it.

'You are beautiful—so, so beautiful . . .' His voice was husky and soft as he put her from him, and the trembling that had taken over her body almost seemed to have affected his too, before she blinked and the illusion faded away. 'And I want you very much. So if we go upstairs . . .' He let his voice trickle away as she flushed hotly. 'You understand? So, this is not a good idea. But it is not good if we talk either, because then we fight— you know?'

Sandi gave him a level look, noticing the faint sparkle of amusement in the black eyes with a tight frown.

'Oh, that look again. *Ma chérie*, we will have to work on that. But for now? For now, we swim. I have to admit to a little subterfuge. I asked Ann if you liked the water and she assured me that you do, that you swim like a little golden fish. My pool is large and warm and very . . . nice.'

His eyebrows quirked at the last word but she still didn't speak. Their conversation had all but reduced her to a weeping mess and his lovemaking had her body quivering like an unset jelly, and now—now he was the cool, debonair, cynical man of the world again, and it hurt far more than it should. But it just proved what she had suspected—that she was nothing more than a momentary pastime, a game, a distraction in his busy life.

They stared at each other for long electric moments without speaking, and then she forced her lips to respond to her mind. 'I don't have a costume.'

'This is no problem. I do not bother with such inconvenient things when I am at home,' he said softly.

'You don't—?' She remembered the dark bronze texture of his magnificent body as he had got out of the pool earlier that day and her face flamed. 'Well, I do,' she said hotly.

'Oh, you English...' He shook his head, his voice wry. 'So conservative, so ashamed of what God has given you. But, as you stated before, I am not ashamed of what He has given me, am I, my reproving little siren? So, you will not be as nature intended, free and silky-smooth in the water? It is wonderful to swim without the constriction of clothes. You have never tried this?'

'No, I have not.' Her tone was vehement and brought a dark sardonic chuckle from the curved mouth.

'Then I am sure we can find you a large concealing T-shirt that will reach down to your knees. Will that do?'

'I'd really rather not,' she said stiffly.

'But you will.' He was absolutely still as he looked down at her, tiny and defiant, in front of him. 'I want you to. Please, Sandi?'

It was the tone in which he spoke rather than his words that crumpled her resistance. He had said she had shown many aspects of her personality, but now she was seeing another side to his—an appealing, almost little-boy-lost side—if a six-foot-plus giant of a man with muscles to match could ever be considered in that light. It was powerful persuasion and she had no defence against such subtleness.

'I—' She hesitated and then shrugged as casually as she could. 'Well, just a quick swim, then. I don't want Ann worrying. And I do want the T-shirt,' she added warningly as he took her hand with a mocking smile and walked her through the back of the house towards the garden.

'Stop worrying. You will have your T-shirt.' They passed through the large French doors of the breakfast room, which directly overlooked a stone patio with hanging baskets and a profusion of flowers in terracotta pots, and then she saw the still waters of the pool glittering under the night sky as Jacques flicked some switches that lit up the whole area with warm golden and pink lights.

The pool was a large one, kidney-shaped, with several tables and chairs and bright parasols at the far end. Behind it stretched a long, low stone building which had obviously once been a barn but was now divided into two rooms. The larger one served as a bar and dining area and the other one, reached through a door from the first, contained several small changing cubicles and showers, complete with a host of swimming costumes to fit every shape and size, numerous thick towelling robes and a large shelf that ran the whole length of the room and was filled to overflowing with different types of shampoo, shower gel, talcum powder and everything else a would-be swimmer could possibly desire.

'Oh . . .' She glanced up at Jacques as she stepped into the room.

'You see?' He waved his hand expansively at the costumes. 'Happy now? You can cover up that delectable body as much or as little as you wish. I will wait for you in the pool,' he added with mocking amusement. 'In case you think I may be tempted to peek.' She felt she ought to glare at him, but instead she found herself giving a weak smile that she immediately despised herself for. 'And if you feel the need for still further protection there are plenty of T-shirts in the cupboard at the end of the room,' he drawled lazily.

'I'm sure a swimming costume will be more than adequate,' she said primly, her face flushing still more as he gave a chuckle of deep, sardonic amusement before leaving her alone.

How on earth had she come to be here? She stood for a moment, gazing at her reflection in one of the long, narrow mirrors that were dotted about the room. The expensive cocktail dress gave her a poise that she had badly needed tonight, and now she was going to strip off both the dress and her inhibitions and make herself

vulnerable. She must be mad. She *was* mad. She blinked
at the slender, golden-haired girl in the mirror. She was
playing with fire here, she really was—and yet she didn't
seem able to drop the matches...

'Oh, hell.' She grimaced into the violet-blue eyes as
panic clutched at her throat. 'What are you doing, Sandi
Gosdon?'

Jacques was already in the water when she emerged, with
slow, tentative steps, from the barn, his dark figure
cutting through the water with a power that made the
panic rise again. He was so masculine, so virile, so...
So in control. As Ian had been in control. Cool, suave,
cynical—but with that edge that made them both different from the normal run-of-the-mill man.

She met lots of men in her working life, some
handsome, some interestingly attractive and some just
plain creeps. But Jacques was different. He had a certain
something that she couldn't put a name to but which
held a potency that would affect any female from sixteen
to sixty. Ian had had it too.

However much she despised the thought of the man
she had married, loathed the fact that she had given him
a right to her mind and her body, she had to acknowledge
that he had been devastatingly attractive. But it had been
skin-deep, only skin-deep. Underneath there had been
the putrid stench of betrayal, dishonesty, trickery and a
treachery that was unimaginable to the normal mind.

She didn't imagine that Jacques was capable of the
sort of cruelty Ian had exacted, but... She stood in the
shadows watching the powerful, steady strokes of his
arms through the rippling water. But his values weren't
hers. He had had women, lots of women; he lived a
bachelor life that he revelled in, apparently with
Monique's blessing.

Monique. She thought again of Jean-Pierre's words
spoken so innocently a few hours before as they had

watched the two entwined in each other's arms. 'They make a handsome couple, do they not? Whenever I see them together like this I am always surprised Monique does not quit the rat race of modelling and concentrate on the Challier fortune instead.' Well, one day she would. Sandi's mouth hardened. Of course she would. They were suited, after all.

The water was as silky-soft as Jacques had promised, and icy-cold on her overheated skin. She gave a little gasp as she slid carefully into the water and then a startled scream as Jacques's head popped up beside her in the next instant, pulling her against him and kissing her hard with wet lips. 'You were at the other end of the pool,' she accused him when his mouth left hers, and then all further thought left her as the feel of his body next to hers broadcast the fact that he, unlike her, wore nothing but his skin.

'You look wonderful.' His eyes were glittering black orbs in the dim pink and golden lights, his face dark and strangely alien. 'Why did you hesitate before you came in?'

'You were watching me?' She had thought he was absorbed in his swimming and hadn't noticed her in the shadow of the building as she had contemplated his dark body in the water.

'All the time,' he said huskily. 'I like to watch you.' His body was providing ample evidence to corroborate his words, and she was glad of the cooling effects of the water as her skin burnt hotly at the feel of his arousal against the smooth silk of her swimsuit.

And then he let her go, turning from her to swim with measured, powerful strokes down the pool, his dark head just visible above the water. 'Come on.' He stopped halfway and raised his arm as he called her. 'Show me how golden-haired temptresses swim.'

She had always been a strong, vigorous swimmer and now she put everything she had into the exercise, driving her body through the water as hard as she could and passing him with a fluid grace that made her honey-coloured limbs appear weightless. She was aware of him at her side as she continued to the far end of the pool, but didn't stop until she reached the smooth marble wall, where she flicked back her hair, which had worked loose from its high knot at the violent movement.

'I'm impressed.' He touched a wayward curl that had fallen across her forehead as he spoke. 'You swim like a man.'

'Is that supposed to be a compliment?' she asked with mock seriousness.

'Not a feminist too?' He shut his eyes for a second, and when he opened them they were bright with suppressed laughter. 'I really don't think I can take much more—my ego is in tatters as it is.'

'That'll be the day.' Now she was laughing openly, and for the next half an hour, as they swam and dived and enjoyed the freedom the water gave their bodies, she almost forgot that she had to be on her guard with this man—almost, but not quite.

'Coffee?' She was just beginning to shiver and he immediately noticed, pulling himself out of the pool with a supreme disregard for his nakedness and offering her his hand as he bent down to the water's edge.

She tried to concentrate her gaze on his upper torso but it was difficult. Her eyes seemed to have a will of their own and she suddenly felt like a naughty little schoolgirl who was spying on her elders. Ridiculous! She blinked at the thought. Absolutely ridiculous. But the sight of that big male body was doing something to her hormones that was creating a soft, moist warmth at the core of her being and sending her heartbeat haywire.

He pulled her out of the pool with effortless ease and then she was standing by him, her limbs shaking and quivering—and not just with the cold. 'The more I see of you, the more I want you,' he said softly. 'You have bewitched me, my cold little English blonde who turns to fire in my arms.'

She wanted to speak, to make some clever, cynical remark that would defuse the sudden electricity and make him turn from her, but her mouth was dry and her heart was pounding like a sledgehammer as she stared up into his face. She was vitally aware of every part of his big masculine body even though her eyes were fixed on his, and the knowledge of his male power over her soft femininity was both intimidating and thrilling, making her helplessly afraid and fascinated at the same time.

'I don't like the thought that other men have touched you, kissed you,' he continued huskily. 'You know that? I have never felt this way before and I don't like it, but I can do nothing about it.'

He meant Ian, she knew he meant Ian, and suddenly the name was a talisman to hold off this feeling that was utterly new to her, this fierce, deep, primitive desire that had a vibrant sexual awareness at its base, and something else—something she didn't recognise.

'You mean my husband?' she asked flatly, forcing the words out of her mouth.

'Your dead husband,' he corrected softly, his face hardening at her tone. 'He's dead, Sandi. Dead. Whatever you shared, however good it was, it is over.'

'I know that.' She swung away from him, the pain in her eyes at the terrible irony visible.

'No, no, I do not think you do.' He caught her arm, forcing her to turn and face him, his eyes black pools in the shadowed light. 'You cannot live on memories; do you not understand this yet? I am not suggesting that you forget this man—I know that would be impossible—but you have to accept that it is over—'

'Leave me alone!' She had thought she could use Ian as protection against Jacques's advances, but she realised now that she was not as strong as she had thought. The bitter humiliation, the doubt, the uncertainty of herself

as a woman, the sense of abject failure—they all crowded in on her as though it were yesterday.

Ian had made her feel as though she was less than dust on the ground when he had taken her innocence and used her before leaving without a word. She had trusted him, loved him, and suddenly it had all been proved a monstrous illusion.

For weeks and months she had walked the streets at night, too tense and emotionally raw to sleep, looking at other women—ugly women, plain women—and wondering what they had that made them so different from her, how men could love them and feel such disgust for her. Because that was what Ian had done for her, she realised now, with a stab of pain that blinded her to Jacques's face. He had made her feel as though she was only fit to be despised, rejected, at best pitied. She was nothing. He had proved it. She was some sort of freak, unlovable and unloved.

'Sandi?'

'*No!*' Suddenly, Jacques faded and Ian stood there, and she reacted with all the hurt, pain and bitterness in her heart. She flew at him, pounding his chest with her fists as she wailed her agony to the moon, and he was still for one stunned moment, then moved swiftly, gathering her up against him as he trapped her wrists in one broad hand and lifted her off her feet with the other, carrying her quickly towards the house.

When she had felt her feet leave the ground the urge to bite and kick and destroy had left her in one blinding surge of tears, and now, as she was carried, she continued to cry, not in acceptable ladylike sobs, but in great convulsive bellows of grief and pain and rage that she had never allowed herself before. She raged against the unfairness of it all, against the agony that should never have been hers to endure. She hadn't done anything— she *hadn't*. She was innocent of it all and yet it was she who had paid the price. It wasn't *fair* . . .

'Drink this.' She wasn't aware that they had entered the house, but a moment or two after she had felt herself being laid on something soft she found that her hand was being raised and made to grasp a glass. Jacques's hold was still tight on her fingers as he raised it to her lips. 'Drink it, Sandi, all of it.'

The neat brandy hit the back of her throat like fire and she spluttered most of the first mouthful all over him, but after trying again, more slowly this time, she managed to swallow several mouthfuls of the raw alcohol before falling back against the soft upholstery of the sofa Jacques had placed her on, her eyes still streaming.

'Now stop crying—that's enough. Do you hear me, Sandi? This is enough.'

She didn't hear the actual words, but the tone of his voice and the feel of his warm flesh against hers as he put the glass down and took her hands in his caused the weeping to subside into hiccuping sobs and then soft, shaking shivers. 'That is it. It is finished—over. Now, you sit here, you do not move, and I will get a cup of coffee, yes?'

As he spoke she forced her swollen eyelids open, knowing that she must look as bad as she felt. She had never been able to cry prettily, not even tears of happiness. Her nose always went red and ran, her eyes swelled and her face turned blotchy. 'I— I'm sorry.' A late and lone sob caught at the words. 'I didn't mean to do this. I don't—'

'It is I who should apologise. I was stupid and clumsy and I spoke of things I had no right to speak of.'

'No.' She peered at him, a thread of surprise at the quiet, almost tender note in his voice piercing her misery. 'It was me. I don't know why I reacted like that. You must think I'm mad, crazy.'

'No, I do not think this.' He was kneeling in front of her, his hands still holding hers. 'What I do think is that all that pain has been held in too long—far, far too long.'

'I—' The sympathy was too much, and as her eyes swam with tears again he stood up briskly, his voice firmer now.

'Coffee. This will make you feel better.'

With Jacques standing as he was, it was impossible for her to concentrate on anything other than his body, and now she surprised them both as she gave a weak smile, her face still wet with tears. 'Are you going to put anything on first?' she asked shakily. 'If you're handling hot liquid?'

'I see your point.' He smiled, a dark, rueful smile directed against himself, and it was in that moment that something in her leapt and sprang into life, but she didn't question what. 'The big seduction scene did not go quite according to plan, did it?' he said mockingly. 'I do not usually have the effect of reducing women to tears when I undress.'

'I'm sure you don't.' The dry humour was restoring her equilibrium, but with it the knowledge that she had just made the most terrible fool of herself began to gather steam. She shut her eyes tight against the sight of him and leant back against the sofa, giving a little shiver that came from the turmoil within her rather than the cool air.

'You are cold.' She heard him move away as he spoke, his bare feet light on the thick carpet, and when in the next instant she found herself enveloped in something soft and warm she still didn't open her eyes.

'Thank you.'

'And now I will get the coffee.'

He was still standing in front of her—she could feel it—and when the silence continued she opened her eyes warily to see him looking down at her with a strange expression on his dark face as she lay curled up in the folds of a blanket.

'It is not a crime to show your feelings, Sandi—you understand this?'

'I know.' She wished to goodness that he would put some *clothes* on, she thought frantically as he remained in front of her. She knew the French had few inhibitions, that *au naturel* was commonplace on the beaches of France, but right now his total disregard for his nakedness was causing her severe breathing problems— and he wanted a conversation about feelings?

'No, you do not know this. You are like the oyster that is tightly closed against the sea of life, holding onto its pearl at all costs.'

'And what happens when the oyster is forced to let go of its pearl?' she asked as coolly as her racing emotions would allow. 'It loses everything.'

'And this is what you feel?' he asked slowly. 'That if you open up, start to live again, you will lose everything for the second time?'

He didn't understand—she knew he didn't understand—but in spite of that he was so near the mark that she stared at him with huge violet-blue eyes opened wide in her tear-stained face. 'Jacques—' She shook her head slowly as her eyes wavered and then fell from his. 'I really can't talk about this right now—I just can't.'

Was he really concerned about the way she was feeling for her sake, or was it the ultimate goal of getting her into his bed that was prompting all this solicitude? she asked herself faintly. He had made no secret of what he was, how he ran his life and more especially his love-life.

Just an hour or so ago, when they had arrived at the farmhouse, he had mentioned the fact that he was often away for days at a time, and irrespective of whether it was because of business or something of a more personal nature he couldn't have made it more clear that a permanent relationship was out of the question. Some women could enjoy such a man, take the time they had together and savour it to the full and then move on when the time came for a parting of the ways with a kiss and a hug.

But she wasn't like that. She never had been. She couldn't envisage ever opening up her mind and her body to anyone again, but if she did ever come to such a point it would have to be with a man who would commit himself to her totally.

She felt him move silently out of the room and when she raised her head she felt almost bereft for a moment. But that will pass, she told herself fiercely. It will.

When he brought in the tray of coffee a few minutes later he was clothed in tight black jeans, his upper torso and feet bare, and although her senses still gave a hard kick at the sight of his muscled, hair-roughened chest and broad, masculine shoulders it wasn't so bad as having all of that magnificent body on display. He didn't speak until he handed her the coffee, but she had felt his eyes intent on her wan face as soon as he'd entered the room.

'Sugar?' His flesh was warm as it touched hers, and she felt the contact with a jolt.

'Two, please.'

He seated himself next to her when he had poured his own cup and as she went to move her legs to the floor he caught at them, his hand resting on top of the blanket. 'No, don't move; it is all right.'

His hand remained on her upper leg, and although the soft cloth was between his flesh and her body she felt the contact begin to burn like fire. She had expected further questioning, or maybe a follow-up on the seduction scene he himself had mentioned earlier, but as they sat in the quiet, beautiful room in the soft, dim light he said nothing, seemingly lost in his own thoughts as he drank the coffee.

She glanced at him once or twice from under her lashes. His hard profile was just a foot or so away, and she found it gave her pleasure to watch him. After the swim his hair was ruffled across his forehead in unruly curls that were as black as jet, and his dark lashes and hard jaw, where the stubble was already showing black under the skin, were curiously sensuous. She wished things could have been different. She wished she had met him years ago, before Ian, when she had still had the ability to believe in love and happy ever after—

The dangerousness of her thoughts suddenly brought her up sharp, the breath catching in her throat. What was she thinking? What *was* she thinking? It didn't matter when she might have met him—he would still have been the same. He wasn't a slippers-by-the-fire man any more than Ian had been. How many times did she have to learn the same lesson before it sank in?

Her thoughts made her swing her feet to the floor abruptly, dislodging his hand, and then she stood up, still keeping the blanket swathed about her.

'I'll go and change now, if that's all right?'

'Of course.' He rose too, his voice cool, but then, as he looked down at her, his eyes crinkled in a smile. 'You look remarkably like a small, worried child, standing there wrapped in that thing,' he said mildly.

'Do I?' She didn't like the simile; she didn't like it at all. She couldn't imagine any man ever saying that to Monique. The tall redhead would look every inch a woman no matter how much or how little of her slim, perfect body was hidden.

'Sandi...' And then his voice changed, thickened, and he drew her against him, his eyes soft. 'Are you warm now?'

'Yes...' Warm? She was on fire, she thought helplessly as she felt his hands move under the folds of the blanket and slide down her body in a slow caress that brought an immediate languorous warmth snaking through her limbs. She had been waiting for this. The thought hit her like a small electric shock. Waiting for it, wanting it—

'I don't know what it is about you that makes me want you so much,' he muttered thickly. 'Oh, Sandi...'

His mouth drove down on hers and at that point all coherent thought stopped. She felt the blanket slide to the floor but hardly registered the fact, although it meant that she was pressed against him in nothing more than a brief black cut-away swimming costume which, in spite of its lack of material, had been the only garment she'd been able to find that went even a little way towards covering her body.

But now that didn't matter—nothing mattered but the mindless pleasure she was experiencing as his powerful body subdued all resistance. The kiss was deep and slow as he invaded the tender, secret places of her half-open mouth, his tongue devastatingly sensuous, and as his hands continued to wander over her skin she felt her breasts fill and harden, their peaks becoming rock-hard when his fingers paused in their exploration of her quivering softness.

'I cannot believe what you do to me...' The sultry French accent added to the magic of what was happening to her. 'You are incredible, incredible...'

His kisses were burning her now as he moved from her mouth to her throat, her ears and then lower, to where the swell of her breasts was straining against the thin fabric of the costume. She knew the thin straps had been pulled down over her shoulders, but still the shock as his lips branded the heavy fullness of her breasts was fierce.

She hadn't known she could feel like this—that the combination of hard male strength and tender love-making could reduce her to a quivering, helpless mass of sheer sensation. She had heard of such things happening to other women, read about the experience second-hand in romantic novels and books, but it was real, *real* . . .

Her hands were laced in his hair now, and as he raised his head again she knew she was murmuring little, soft, incoherent pleas against his lips. But she could no more control her mind than her body. She was on fire, on fire, and she had no idea how it had all come about.

'Sandi?' For a moment she couldn't believe that he had moved her gently from him to arm's length, but as she opened dazed blue eyes and saw him looking down at her she was quite unable to speak. 'One more moment and I shan't be able to stop. You understand what I am saying? Whether you want me to or not I shall have you, but it will be *me*, Jacques Challier, not some shadow that you have conjured out of your mind. Listen to me, Sandi . . .'

Listen to him? She stood swaying, her skin flushed a deep, warm pink, as she tried to make sense of what he was saying.

'I will not be used as a substitute. This I will not allow.' A substitute? she thought faintly. What on earth was he talking about? 'When I have you—and I *will* have you— it will be because you want me as badly as I want you. Whatever you shared with your husband, however much you loved him, he will not be a spectre at our union. I will not have it.'

'I—' She tried to speak, to communicate in some way, but both her mind and body seemed transfixed and her eyes fell from his as she tried to focus her thoughts.

'*Look at me.*' His voice was harsh now, in direct contrast to the softness of before. 'Look at *me*. I am alive. I am flesh and blood—feel.' He took one of her limp hands and banged it against his chest. 'You see?'

'Don't.' She shrank from him, from the anger in his face.

'I want you, Sandi.' His voice was tight and strained. 'I want you so badly I can taste it, but not at the cost of my self-respect.'

He took her arm now, leading her from the room and through to the grounds at the back of the house without speaking. He opened the door of the changing room, almost thrust her inside and turned to leave.

'Jacques?' She was stunned, bewildered at the sudden turn events had taken.

'Get dressed, Sandi.' His voice was harsh and cold now, his self-control visible in the steely tightness of his jaw and the way he held his big, hard body rigid and taut. 'I'll wait in the car.'

And then he left her, slamming the door behind him with a viciousness which indicated that the self-control was only just holding out.

CHAPTER SEVEN

'YOU'RE leaving today? But why?'

Sandi reached across the small table on their suite's balcony and took Ann's hands in her own as her sister stared at her, her face and voice heavy with disappointment. 'I need to get back to work, Ann,' she said quietly. 'They have been very good about all this, but it's been nearly three weeks now, and there are a hundred people who would be only too pleased to step into my shoes—you know how things are in the advertising world. You are happy here, settled, and that's all I wanted to be sure about before I left. There's no need for me to stay here now.'

'I'll miss you.' Ann looked at her, her voice flat. 'It won't be the same with you gone.'

'But you knew I couldn't stay.' Sandi squeezed her sister's hands. 'That was never on the cards, was it? You get on so well with Arianne and Odile, besides which it won't be two minutes before I'm back to see my nephew or niece.'

'Yes, I know.' Ann sighed and looked down at the table on which the remains of their breakfast were sitting. 'And I do appreciate you coming over here with me instead of going straight back to America—it helped enormously.'

Not me, Sandi thought wryly with silent pain. It hasn't helped me at all.

When Jacques had brought her back to the château the night before she had expected him to come in, but he had merely left the car to open her door and see her across the threshold before turning to leave. 'Where are you going?' Her voice had been high with surprise as she had spoken to his departing back.

'Home.' He had turned halfway to the car as she had stood in the doorway watching him. 'My home.'

'But—' He wasn't going to leave like this, was he? she thought miserably. Without a word being exchanged? Without things being sorted? 'I thought—' She stopped again. The glittering black eyes weren't conducive to conversation.

'You thought what?' he asked as he moved to stand in front of her, his great height dwarfing her petiteness. 'You thought I would beg, is that it?'

'Beg?' She reared up in surprise and distaste. 'I don't know what you mean.'

'Do you not?' He was looking at her intently, his eyes narrowed and dark in the shadows of his tanned face as he stood with his back to the moonlight. 'Well, perhaps you do and perhaps you do not, my English rose, but it really doesn't matter one way or the other. You have made it perfectly clear how you feel and, unlike many others of my sex, I have never indulged in the strange fancy of banging my head against a brick wall.'

'Banging your head...?' She was still staring at him in bewilderment as he gave a harsh sigh of deep exasperation then leant forward and kissed her—a hard, bruising kiss that spoke of anger and fury—seconds before he turned from her and strode to his car. The engine started immediately, and in almost the same instant the Ferrari swung in a violent semi-circle to roar off down the drive in a flurry of screaming tyres and silver metal, leaving her small and forlorn on the doorstep.

Those feelings were soon replaced by a multitude of others as she got ready for bed in the luxurious sitting room to avoid waking Ann, who was fast asleep in the bedroom. Bewilderment, rage, bitterness, fury, pain, resentment... The list was endless. She methodically showered and brushed her teeth in the lovely bathroom a few minutes later, narrowing her eyes at her reflection in the mirror over the sink. He was angry with her, that much was obvious, and why? Because she hadn't slept with him. It was as simple as that. And why hadn't she slept with him? She rinsed the toothpaste away and then sipped at a glass of water as she looked into the large violet-blue eyes in the mirror. Because he had stopped making love to her.

She shut her eyes, but when she opened them again the reproachful look was still there. After all she had said, all her high intentions, that was what it boiled down to. He could have had her back there at his house and she wouldn't have stopped him, and he had known that— he had. So, if that was the case, how dared he blame her for the ugly end to the evening?

She glared ferociously into the mirror, her brow wrinkling. *He* had stopped, *he* had started talking about substitutes and goodness knew what, and then he had blamed her for it all, acting as though she were a tease, as though she expected him to beg. She hadn't realised how much that word—'beg'—rankled until he had left. How dared he? How *dared* he act like that?

Then later, as she lay curled up in bed with Ann's steady, rhythmic breathing mocking her wakefulness, the tears came. Hot, scalding tears that burnt her face and stung her eyes. And much much later, as dawn began to make its way across the window in a pink-grey glow, she realised she had to leave this place, get as far away from Jacques Challier as possible. Immediately.

'How are you getting back?'

She came back to the present with a jolt and forced herself to smile at Ann as she replied as lightly as she could. 'By plane. It's quicker and less time-consuming. I've got a taxi coming at eleven to pick me up.'

'As organised as ever.' Ann glanced over the rolling lawns and tree-filled grounds as she spoke.

'I've always had to be, haven't I?' There was a slight touch of bitterness in the words. Since their parents had died, and she had taken on the role of both mother and father to her younger sister, all the onus had been on her to guide and direct their lives. And although she hadn't minded that, recognising that Ann's placid, quiet nature wasn't able to cope with any big decisions, the responsibility had been enormous at times. And after Ian's death it had been worse, somehow—infinitely worse—because she had doubted her ability to make even the simplest decision for a time, her self-esteem and faith in herself at rock-bottom.

'Are you going straight back to the States?' Ann now asked as she turned to look at her again, her hands on the mound of her stomach and the expression on her face one of quiet repose. 'I thought if you went back to England first you could settle the matter of the flat and—'

'No, sorry; I'm going straight home.' Sandi straightened as she spoke. She needed to get as far away as she could, and England wasn't far enough. Not that she thought Jacques would come after her. Of course he wouldn't—he had made it perfectly clear last night exactly what he thought of her—but nevertheless . . .

She just wanted to get back to her small apartment, her little car and her job. Normality. Safety. Everything that she suddenly desperately needed. 'I brought everything with me to France so there's no reason to go to England—it would be a waste of money. You only need to settle the matter of the flat by phone, anyway—you always pay a month in advance so there'll be no problems, Ann.'

'No, I guess not.' Ann smiled at her suddenly. 'And it's about time I started doing a few things on my own initiative, isn't it? Especially with junior on the way. Emile always said I would be capable of far more than I realised if I just pushed myself a little.'

'He was right.' Sandi stood up and moved round the small table to give her sister a hug. 'But don't push yourself too much in your condition,' she added wryly. 'Just take it nice and easy and everything will work out fine.' She suddenly felt as if one great weight had been lifted off her mind. If Ann could begin to think along those lines it boded nothing but good for the future and her child.

The other great weight, however, remained firmly in place, and she wrinkled her eyes against the image of Jacques Challier which confronted her the whole time she packed.

The taxi drew into the Challier estate on the dot of eleven, and Sandi left the château amid a host of hugs and kisses from Ann, Arianne and Odile, Claude and André having already left for the vineyards. Anna-Marie, Suzanne and Antoinette were particularly loath to let their new-found friend go, each little girl insisting on a long cuddle and kiss and making her promise that she would come back soon and see them.

'I shall come back and see all of you—and your new cousin when it's born,' Sandi assured them as she climbed into the taxi, her eyes bright with unshed tears as the three infants stood in a row by the door, their dark curls and huge brown eyes making them appear angelic. As their mother translated her words to them they all nodded with gusto, and then the taxi was drawing away. After waving through the back window until she could see them no more she leant back against the upholstered seat, swamped by a wave of misery.

She was confused, bewildered and unhappy, and somewhere in the back of her mind she felt that she had been dreadfully unfair to Jacques—although she wasn't sure how. He knew she wasn't game for a little light affair—she couldn't have made it more obvious from minute one—and she had been honest with him—almost. He had jumped to the conclusion that she was still in love with Ian, and although admittedly she had gone along with the supposition the end result would still have been the same even if she had told him the whole truth. Which she couldn't have done.

She twisted in the seat as she hugged her waist tight, the pain engendered by her thoughts almost physical. She just couldn't have done. The humiliation of that time, the terrible abasement and degradation she had felt—she couldn't expose them to the light of day for anyone, ever. She couldn't.

Once back in America, Sandi settled into the daily panic and drama of advertising life as though she had never been away, although even in the midst of the worst pandemonium and bedlam she was conscious of a deep, hard ache in her chest that just wouldn't go away. She worked late every night, only leaving the offices when she was ready to drop with exhaustion, knowing that that was the only way sleep could be guaranteed.

Even so, when she awoke each morning as soon as it grew light she was aware that she hadn't slept well.

But she was happy. She told herself so every morning without fail when she glared fiercely at her reflection in the mirror as she got ready for work. Happy, and contented with the way her life was going. *She was*. The blue-eyed reflection didn't argue but the violet gaze was always misted with tears when she eventually turned away.

She phoned Ann three or four times a week and was more reassured each time she spoke to her sister that she was going to be all right. So—everything in the garden was lovely. Of course it was.

She had been back in the States for four weeks when she opened an envelope one morning in order to process some shots from a top fashion show the day before and Monique's cool, unsmiling face stared back at her from the catwalk. She sat staring at the beautiful redhead for a full minute before she raised her head and buzzed the main office for Andy, the young assistant she had sent with the photographer for that particular shoot. 'Andy? That fashion show yesterday...'

'Yes?' He was immediately by her desk. 'Is anything wrong? They're doing something with those models each day this week for the Zac promotion, so if you don't like these shots—'

'No, no—the photographs are fine,' she answered absently. 'You say the girls are here for the week—all of them?'

'That's right.' He stared at her, puzzled.

'OK, thanks, Andy.' She sat staring at the prints for a full minute more before bundling them together and sending them to one of her co-executives to process. She didn't feel she could be unbiased. She was determined that personal feelings wouldn't interfere with her professional judgement, but somehow she felt that the redhead had invaded her world deliberately.

She was still thinking about the photographs when she arrived home that evening, parking her neat little car in the underground car park before walking into the foyer of her apartment block.

'Miss Gosdon?' The uniformed security man called her as she prepared to enter the lift without looking to left or right, her mind a million miles away. 'This gentleman has been waiting to see you for the last three hours.'

Whether it was the fact that Monique's appearance in America was still firmly in the forefront of her mind or that she had been thinking about Jacques Challier—consciously and subconsciously—for every minute of the day and night since she had left France she didn't know, but as she turned and saw him standing to one side of a large coffee-table littered with magazines and empty paper cups she found that she wasn't as surprised as she should have been.

'*Bonjour*, Sandi.' The voice was deep and silky, with that little edge she remembered. Oh, how she remembered it, she thought shakily as she looked into the hard, dark face with a feeling of impending doom.

He looked wonderful—but then of course he would, she thought bitterly. He was obviously accompanying Monique on her modelling assignment and enjoying every moment, if that cool, confident smile was anything to go by. His personality was powerful enough as it was, but the fact that his world was clearly right on course infuriated her still more because she felt that hers, for whatever reason, was most definitely not.

'Jacques? What a nice surprise.' She forced herself to walk forward with her hand outstretched and her voice polite, and she stitched a smile onto her face with tremendous effort. 'What brings you to this neck of the woods?'

'Business.' He looked down at her as she reached him and his eyes were warm. 'They say all good things come to those who wait, and have I been waiting!' He ignored her outstretched hand, gathering her into his arms and kissing her very thoroughly for one long, heart-stopping moment before letting her go. 'Where have you been? It's after nine.'

'Working.' She was hanging onto her composure by the skin of her teeth, but the interested face of the security man kept her voice bland and her face pleasant. 'You should have let me know you were coming. I'd have told you I was busy and bound to be delayed.'

'Perhaps that is why I didn't let you know,' he said drily.

And *perhaps* she was being fitted in between Monique's modelling assignments? she thought tightly. He was transparent; he really was. Didn't he think she could put two and two together and make four? She wouldn't have minded if he'd called round merely in the role of Ann's brother-in-law while he was in America, but that kiss had suggested that he wanted far more than a brotherly welcome.

'How long are you here for?' she asked carefully as she began to walk to the lift with him at her side.

'How long do you want me to stay?' he countered swiftly, with a nod and a smile at the security guard as the doors closed.

'Jacques—' She stopped abruptly and took a hold of her temper, which had risen to boiling point when really she had no right to be annoyed. He was a free agent— he had never pretended to be anything else—and she had nothing to blame him for. All she had to do was be pleasant for an hour or two until he left, no doubt to meet Monique, and treat him courteously while keeping him very firmly at arm's length. It was up to her to set the tone. It was simple, really. 'Just answer the question.' She softened the words with a cool but not unfriendly smile.

'I am here for five days, Sandi.' He looked down at her, his dark face unreadable. Just the amount of time the modelling assignment for Zac Fashions was going to last, she thought silently. She should have known.

He was standing leaning against the side of the lift now as he watched her through dark, narrowed eyes, his hands thrust in the pockets of his fashionable loose-cut trousers and his open-necked shirt displaying the tanned, hard line of his throat.

'And what exactly is the business that brings you all the way to New York?' she asked carefully as the lift doors glided open at her floor, displaying a quiet, wide corridor with ankle-deep carpeting and pale cream linen walls.

'"Exactly"?' His tone mocked her words and he didn't answer immediately, stepping out of the lift and glancing round as he nodded slowly. 'This is very chic. I like this.'

OK, so you like it, she thought snappily as she indicated a door halfway down the corridor with a wave of her hand, but just answer the question, will you? Smooth-talking Frenchman or no, he was going to have a job to explain this one.

'I am here to iron out the details on a new contract with one of our wine merchants that was recently taken over,' he said lazily as they walked side by side to her front door. 'I could have accomplished this by phone but it is always better to do business face to face in these circumstances, besides which . . .' he glanced down at her as she fitted her key into the lock, but she missed the look on his face as she opened the door ' . . . I wanted a few days away from the vineyards and America seemed the perfect place.'

Well, he hadn't exactly lied—she had to give him that, she thought silently as she waved him into her apartment. She didn't doubt for a moment that the explanation of the contract with one of his merchants was true, but he hadn't explained why America was 'the perfect place'.

Monique's beautiful cat-like face rose up in front of her, and her smile was grim as she followed him into the large, comfortable sitting room. She had given him his chance to come clean and if he wanted to play it close to his chest then she was blowed if she was going to force the issue. But she was grateful to the powers that be that she had seen those photographs this afternoon, otherwise she might have thought— She gave a mental shake of her head at her own naïvety. She might have thought he had come all that way to see her.

The knowledge that she could still be such a fool, after all that had happened, made her mouth tight and her eyes strained as she watched him glance round her home. The apartment had already been furnished to a high standard when she had moved in, but although the decor was in neutral, pale shades of cream and beige she had added nothing of herself to make it more personal.

The home she had shared with Ian had been vivid and vibrant, her love of fabric and eye for colour creating a warm oasis that had been both pleasant to live in and beautiful to behold. But when her marriage had exploded in her face something within her had died. She wasn't aware that she had purposely stifled the desire to make any sort of nest, but Jacques, as he glanced around the immaculate, beautiful and sober surroundings, wondered at the puritanical austerity.

'The apartment was furnished when I came.' She was immediately annoyed with herself for feeling the need to explain anything to him, but as he had turned to stare at her she had sensed something in his attitude that she didn't like, almost a kind of pity. 'I find it restful.'

'Yes.' He nodded slowly. 'It is tranquil after all the hurly-burly outside, yes?'

'Exactly.' Her cheeks were burning now—she could feel it—and as she walked through to the small kitchen she found that her stomach was clenched in one giant knot. Why couldn't he leave her alone? She didn't want him here—she didn't. Poking about with those piercing, knowing eyes. Why had he come anyway? Surely Monique was enough for any man to cope with?

'Coffee?' She called the question over her shoulder through to the sitting room, but his voice sounded deep and lazy just behind her in the doorway.

'I have had enough coffee in the last three hours to last me for some time. But please, if you would like one . . . ?'

'A glass of wine, then? Or maybe something stronger?' She nerved herself to turn and face him as she spoke, but was still shocked into immobility for a brief moment at the sight of him, big and dark and sardonic, in her small home. He had brought something with him, quite what she didn't know, but it was turning the air electric and creating a whole horde of tumultuous emotions inside her, not one of which she wanted to examine.

'Wine would be lovely.' He watched her as she turned to the fridge and extracted a bottle from the bottom shelf.

'Have you eaten?' he asked casually as she reached for two glasses from the small cupboard above the long, wide breakfast bar.

'Eaten?' She stared at him as though he had just spoken in a foreign language instead of very acceptable accented English.

'Eaten.' He repeated the word with a patience that bordered on the insulting. 'You know? With a knife and fork, a spoon, your fingers. Transferring food to your mouth—'

'I know what eating means, thank you.' She glared at him and was slightly taken aback when he returned the glare.

'Then could you just say yes or no?' he asked tightly. 'You're as jumpy as a kitten, for crying out loud. What do you think I am going to do? Leap on you and take you here and now on the kitchen floor?'

'Don't be—'

'No, don't you dare use that word again,' he interrupted angrily. '*Ridiculous*. I had never been called ridiculous in my life until I met you, but you know something? You make me feel ridiculous,' he said furiously. 'Ridiculous for bothering to come here, for caring about how you are getting on, for wanting to see you. I did not, for one moment, expect to be received with open arms, but I did expect a little courtesy—'

'I've been courteous!' She was stung into a denial that was more shrill than she would have liked. 'I've invited you in, haven't I?'

'Oh, thank you—thank you so much,' he drawled sarcastically, his voice icy. 'The fact that you are a walking block of stone on two legs is supposed to make me feel good, is that it?'

'I didn't know I was expected to make you feel good,' she said coldly as her heart pounded so hard that she was sure he must hear it. He had Monique for that, surely? she thought bitterly.

'No?' She was suddenly afraid of the coiled tension evident in every line of his big body as he glared at her, his eyes dark and glittering in his angry face. 'Well, perhaps it is up to me to make us both feel good, yes? A little therapeutic lovemaking, maybe?'

She opened her lips to fire back a reply but he moved in the same instant to take her mouth in a fierce, ruthless kiss that spoke of pure, undiluted rage and frustration. She struggled, using her hands and feet as she fought, but he didn't even notice as he moulded her soft shape into the hard lines of his and kept his mouth fixed on hers. And then, in spite of herself, it was happening again. That soft, irresistible melting of her will and her body to his.

One minute she was fighting him with every ounce of her strength, and then she was moving almost wantonly against him, her eyes closed, her face entranced and her body speaking eloquently of her need. His hands were moving all over her body and she wanted them to— wanted him to touch her intimately, fully, to explore every part of her.

'That is enough therapy for now.' She couldn't believe he was moving her from him again—*again*. As her eyes opened dazedly to fix on the hard, ruthless face in front of her she was quite unable to speak, and such was her humiliation and shame that it blinded her to the way his hands were shaking as he deftly adjusted her clothing. 'Now, we will drink a glass of wine and consider which restaurant I am taking you to tonight, yes?'

'No.' She stared at him in disbelief. He didn't really think she was going on a date with him, did he? After the way he'd just behaved, and with Monique lurking somewhere in the background like a tall and very elegant lady vampire? And after rejecting her for the second time? 'I wouldn't go out with you if you were the last man on earth,' she said hotly.

'A little extreme, but I do get the message.' He smiled, apparently not in the least put out. 'In that case we will eat here. I will arrange to have food brought in.'

'I am not spending the evening with you—'

'Oh, but you are, my sweet little English icicle,' he said silkily, his mouth hardening. 'And there is no need to be so incensed because you respond so beautifully to me. It is not a crime to enjoy the pleasures of love, I do assure you. And one day, when I know it is *my* body you are seeing and enjoying and *my* voice you are hearing, I shall not stop. You understand?'

No—no, she didn't understand, she thought helplessly as she glared back at him, but it was clear that he had no intention of leaving, and, short of calling Arthur, the security man, and having him evicted from her apartment, she really didn't know how she could make him leave. And even that wouldn't work, she acknowledged weakly. She doubted if anyone had ever made Jacques Challier do something he didn't want to do in the whole of his life, and poor old Arthur, with his rotund stomach and bad back, would be no match for the younger man.

'You're a pig and a bully,' she said a little desperately.

'And you are being very childish.' He glanced over her with soft mockery, his temper and aplomb remarkably restored after his lovemaking. 'I really don't know whether to smack you or soothe you.'

'You'd better not try either,' she said hastily.

'Don't tempt me, Sandi, and never throw a challenge like that to a man who has just behaved in a chivalrous fashion quite new to him and at great personal cost,' he said with sardonic coolness. 'Now, where is your telephone directory? I will arrange for a quantity of dishes to be brought here. Would you prefer Chinese, Italian, Indian—?'

'No.' As he opened his mouth to speak again she went on hastily, 'And I'm not being awkward, really. I'll cook us something if you insist on staying; your family *are* looking after Ann, after all.'

'Not the most gracious invitation I've ever received,' he said drily, 'but it's a deal. And while you're organising the food I will go and get some decent wine.' He had picked up the bottle of cheap plonk she'd had in the fridge and eyed it with something akin to horror as he had spoken. 'Red or white?'

'White... or red. Either. I don't mind.' She was flustered and stammering, and she could have kicked herself for letting him affect her the way he did. She didn't like the way he made her feel, but she couldn't do anything about it either. Every nerve in her body was sensitised to the point where it was raw and painful, and the flutters of excitement in her stomach and the thudding of her heart were further evidence of her body's betrayal.

Amazingly, in view of the state of her nerves, the soufflé was cooked to perfection, as were the accompanying vegetables. The wine that Jacques had chosen was mellow and fruity and potent, and although the dessert was nothing more exciting than fruit crumble it was, nevertheless, delicious.

She was overwhelmingly thankful that she had gone shopping the night before. Living on his own as he did, Jacques would surely appreciate that her rustling up such a meal at short notice meant that she was both organised and capable as well as independent, she thought hopefully. All reinforcing her image as successful businesswoman? The fact that the night before the fridge had harboured nothing more exciting than two tomatoes and a lump of stale cheese was incidental.

'How did I know you'd cook like an angel?' he asked softly as she prepared to serve him the last portion of the fruit crumble at his request—his third serving.

'You didn't,' she said flatly, placing the bowl in front of him along with the jug of fresh cream.

'Oh, but I did.' He eyed her consideringly. 'I really did. Perhaps it's something to do with that old adage about the way to man's heart being through his stomach?'

'I think they got the part of the anatomy wrong,' she said drily. 'Most of the men I know have their sights set a little lower.'

'I'm shocked.' He laughed at her, his eyes mocking and soft as they wandered over her flushed face.

'Now, that I do doubt,' she said with cryptic wryness. 'I don't think there is much that would shock you, Jacques Challier.' It must have been the wine that had loosened her tongue, she thought a second later as she wrenched her eyes from his bright gaze and drank the last of the richly rounded liquid from her glass.

'In this you are right.' She glanced up to see a strange expression darken the handsome face. 'Not now, at least. But I think it is not good to be...what is the word? Unshockable? Can you say that in English?'

'You just did.' She smiled at him but he didn't return the smile. Instead he leant forward, taking her hands in his as he stared into her face.

'I want to tell you something, Sandi,' he said flatly. 'It may help you to understand the sort of man I am, perhaps to comprehend what you cannot condone.'

'I don't think—'

He stopped her, one hand lifting to her mouth as he placed a quiet finger on her lips. 'Please. You are Ann's sister and a member of my family now whether you like it or not, and I do not think this antagonism between us will be good for the niece or nephew we share.'

Antagonism? she asked herself wryly. Was it antagonism that caused her to melt at his touch? She wished it were—oh, she did. Antagonism she could have coped with, but this sexual attraction that seemed to spring to life every time she saw him—that was something altogether more dangerous.

'When I was younger—much, much younger,' he added with a wry smile, 'I was engaged to be married for a time.' She felt the shock of his words register right down to her toes, but forced herself to remain absolutely still. 'The lady in question was my age—I had met her in my first year at university and we were together every moment from that time.'

'Every moment?' she asked carefully, and he let go of her hands and moved to stand with his back to her as he gazed out of the window at the New York skyline.

'Figuratively speaking,' he said flatly. 'Jacqueline was a free spirit, but by unspoken mutual consent neither of us took other partners.'

'Oh.' It didn't matter—of course it didn't matter, she told herself frantically. He was nothing to her, was he? She didn't even understand why he was telling her this.

'We graduated on the same day, found a flat in Paris, and with money both my parents and hers had loaned us started our own business—a little bistro that did extremely well. After a couple of months we set the wedding date for the beginning of November, when business would be slacker, and on the thirteenth of October she was found dead in the street in an area well-known for its drug addicts and pushers.'

'Drugs?' Sandi stared at his broad back in horror.

'Apparently she had started on the mild sort when she was at university,' he said flatly, his voice expressionless. 'The police discovered she had moved to heroin only a few weeks before her death. The fact that the business was doing so well had enabled her to try something more expensive.

'Her parents were devastated. She was an only child, and, perhaps naturally in the circumstances, they blamed me. They could not believe I hadn't known what she was doing. My own parents were more understanding, but then I was alive—they had not lost their child.'

'But—' She stopped abruptly. 'There weren't any signs?' she asked helplessly, wishing he would turn round so that she could see his face.

'None that I noticed. The final irony was that it was our best friend—a man I had gone through university with and regarded as a brother—who had been the pusher from the start. His guilt at her death led him to make a full confession to the police after they picked him up for another offence. He had, it seems, unknowingly sold Jacqueline a bad fix. His supplier had mixed the heroin with other substances. I understand more than five people died from that one batch.

'But the thing is...' he turned to face her now, and his face was strange in its lack of expression '...I didn't know. I had no idea—about her, about him, about any of it. I had known them both for three years, lived with Jacqueline for five months, and yet I didn't know the first thing about them. You have no idea how that felt.'

Oh, yes, I have, she thought painfully. I have.

'So—I did my penance for a time. The remorse, the guilt, the bitterness—all of it.' Just for a second the mask slipped and she saw a wealth of pain in his eyes. 'And then I decided to get on with life, but under my terms. No more involvement, no more commitment, no more trust. I had tried all that and it hadn't worked, so from then on I decided I would expect nothing and give nothing, and that way, if I made it perfectly clear from the onset, no one would get hurt.'

'Has it worked?' she asked softly.

'Yes.' He looked straight at her. 'Until recently.'

He meant Monique. The shock of what he had told her, the bitterness of betrayal she had glimpsed briefly in his eyes had had her wanting to go to him, to comfort him in some way, to tell him that she *did* understand, but now the thought of the other woman froze her tongue and her heart.

He had made it clear that he had revealed what was obviously a painful and difficult confidence to her because he was worried about the effect their stormy relationship was having on Ann and ultimately her child. That was all. *That was all.* This fiery sexual attraction that flared up between them he could and did control, and to a man like him it meant nothing beyond brief fleshly satisfaction. He had just been most explicit about the way he conducted his life.

She had to accept the fact that he trusted her enough to disclose his past and leave it at that, and as her heart thudded like a sledgehammer and her mind cried out against the unfairness of it all she raised her chin proudly. She loved him. The knowledge was there inside her and she felt no surprise. She had loved him from that moment when he had stood naked before her at his home, after comforting her in her agony of weeping, and had smiled at the joke against himself. She had known then but her mind had fought against the knowledge every step of the way.

'Thank you for telling me all this, Jacques—' Her voice broke but her dignity held intact as she smiled shakily and rose from the table. 'I'm sure it will help us get on better in the future and make things easier for Ann.'

'Ann...' He stared at her, his voice flat.

She turned her head away as though she couldn't look at him, and it was true—she couldn't. The sight of him standing there, the knowledge that she loved him, that she had committed the equivalent of emotional suicide, and the burning jealousy that was filling her whole being at the thought of him with Monique, were too much. 'I'm just going to the bathroom. I won't be a moment.'

He called her name as she left the room but she didn't stop. If she had he would have seen the tears streaming down her face, and that would have been the final humiliation. She had brought this on herself, she had no one else to blame, and now all she could do was get through the rest of the evening with a modicum of self-respect and poise. It would be hard, but then she had faced and overcome so much in the last three years that this one final hurdle would not be beyond her. She couldn't let it be.

CHAPTER EIGHT

'SANDI?' Andy's voice was right in her ear before her brain acknowledged the sound, bringing her back from her miserable reflection on the night before.

She had been a full ten minutes in the bathroom before she'd been sure that all trace of her tears had vanished, and when she had re-entered the sitting room Jacques had been sitting in an easy chair close to the window, contemplating a night sky that was alive with high-rise blocks in which small squares of lights had glowed brilliantly against the dusky blackness.

He hadn't smiled as she had joined him—in fact he hadn't smiled for the rest of the fifteen minutes or so that he had stayed—and had left almost immediately after a polite, cool speech of appreciation for the meal that had been stilted and formal. She had sat for hours after he had gone, the littered table and half-drunk wine remaining exactly as they were, before eventually stumbling to bed after she had cried herself dry, there to lie awake with wide, burning eyes until it had been time to get up.

'I'm sorry, Andy.' She forced herself to concentrate as her junior's concerned young face peered down at her. 'I was miles away.'

'Are you all right?' He had never seen his boss anything but one hundred per cent efficient, and this wan, lethargic woman who had been on a different planet all morning was worrying.

'I'm fine, thank you. Now, what's the problem?' Sandi answered briskly, appreciating the concern but knowing

that the slightest show of sympathy this morning would
have her howling like a baby.

'It's these photos for *Rage* magazine. I don't think
they'll do...'

By the end of the long day her head was thudding, she
felt hot and unbearably sticky, in spite of the excellent
air-conditioning, and more exhausted than she could ever
remember having felt. The final straw was Reception
calling through just as everyone was leaving and telling
her she had a visitor, which caused her to snap down
the phone, her voice terse, 'There is no way I can see
anyone this evening, Belinda. Tell whoever it is to make
an appointment for tomorrow.'

'I don't think I can.' Belinda, that model of ice-cool
efficiency and chilling sternness, who fended off un-
wanted visitors every day of her life, sounded ruffled.
'He's most persistent.'

'I don't care.' Sandi closed her eyes suddenly and took
a hold of herself. Poor Belinda—she must sound like a
real shrew. 'Look, I'm sorry. If he's being difficult I'll
send Andy down with my appointment diary and fix
something up for tomorrow, OK? Don't worry.'

'Right, thanks.' Belinda sounded most relieved, and
Sandi shook her head and leant back in her chair for a
moment, shutting her eyes against the pain in her skull.
It was unusual for anyone to throw their wonder of a
receptionist; he really must be determined. Damn—she
hadn't even asked his name, she thought suddenly. Now,
why on earth hadn't Belinda told her?

She ground her teeth with an irritation which
heightened as she caught sight of Andy through the glass
partition which separated her office from the main one.
He was just walking out of the door, deep in conversation with several colleagues, the door closing behind
them in the next instant.

Oh, wonderful—the perfect end to a perfect day, she thought tightly. Now she would have to go down to Reception herself, and she still had at least another two hours of work to get through before she could go home. Her brain just hadn't seemed able to retain any information today, and everything had taken her twice as long.

Should she ring down and ask Belinda to send this person up? she wondered. She might as well, otherwise she was going to have to go down to Reception to see him. She sucked in air between her teeth in an irritable sigh. Well, she'd give him ten minutes and that was all. She was going to be here till way past seven as it was.

She was immersed in a long transcript of a dissertation from an important Japanese link that tentatively promised an enormous potential contract when the sharp knock at her open door snapped her head upright.

'The formidable Belinda said I was admitted to the holy of holies,' Jacques drawled laconically, and watched her mouth and eyes open wide.

'You?' She gaped at him before realising she must look like a surprised goldfish, whereupon she shut her mouth quickly.

'Me.' He entered the office with lazy assurance and seated himself in the chair opposite her desk.

'But—' She stared at him for a second more. 'She didn't say—you didn't say—'

'If you are trying to ask if I gave my name, the answer is no,' he said without a shred of embarrassment. 'I told her I was your boyfriend, who'd arrived in the States for a couple of days and wanted to surprise you.'

'And she believed that?' Sandi asked in amazement.

'Of course.' He smiled mockingly. 'I can lie very convincingly when I want to, and the knowledge that you would send me away with—what is that revolting English expression?—a flea in the ear if I told her who I was made me most persuasive.'

'How do you know what I would have done?' she asked tightly as the blood pounded in her ears and her heart thudded against her ribcage like an imprisoned bird. Be calm, be cool, she told herself silently. Don't give yourself away. But it was hard to return to their old pattern of verbal sparring when all she wanted to do was fling herself into his arms.

'*Touché*, Miss Gosdon.' He bowed his head slightly and his black eyes continued to watch her. 'Would you have?' he suddenly enquired. 'Sent me away?'

'No.' It was out before she could stop it, and she followed on hastily, 'Of course I wouldn't. You are Ann's brother-in-law, for goodness' sake.'

'Damn Ann's brother-in-law!' The words were in the form of a mini explosion and she winced at the force of them. 'I asked you if you would see *me*, Jacques Challier,' he said with icy control after taking a long, deep breath. 'That is quite different and you know it.'

'Jacques—'

'Do not bother to reply.' The smile was as cold as his face, which held no amusement in its arctic depths. 'Your face adequately speaks for you.'

She hoped not—oh, she did hope not, she thought painfully as he shifted in the chair and glanced round the outer office, his profile hard and unyielding. If her face was portraying even a glimmer of what she was really feeling at this moment in time he would be horrified, she thought bleakly. Horrified and embarrassed to think he was being burdened by anything more than mutual sexual attraction.

'So this is where you work.' He turned his gaze back to her, but she could read nothing, good or bad, in the black eyes. 'I am impressed.'

She shrugged and smiled, not knowing how to reply even if she could have forced words past the constriction in her throat. She hadn't expected to see him again until Ann's baby was born, if then, and now here he was not a foot away from her. She wanted to drink in the sight of him—the black curly hair, hard square jaw and big, masculine shoulders—but she forced her eyes to drop to the papers on her desk before she gave herself away.

'When will you be finished?' He waved his hand at her desk as she glanced up at him. 'I would like to take you out to dinner—just dinner,' he added sarcastically as she flushed hotly. 'I will pick you up about eight at your apartment, so be ready.'

'How do you know I haven't got something planned already?' she asked shortly as the cool male arrogance, the imperious assumption that she was free, made her suddenly mad.

'Have you?'

'No.'

'Eight, then.' He rose as he spoke and reached the open door before turning round to survey her through glittering eyes. 'And it would make for a good evening if you could at least pretend to enjoy my company for once.'

'If you feel like that, why ask me out to dinner in the first place?' she asked, with more than a touch of acerbity in her voice. And to think she had spent a sleepless night and a miserable day over this monster. She was crazy, stupid—

'I would dearly love to know the answer to that question myself.' He eyed her sardonically. 'Put it down to the fact that I can't bear the thought that there is a woman who is oblivious to my accomplished charms. Will that do?' He raised his dark eyebrows as he watched her struggle to form a reply, and left while she was still spluttering.

That evening set the pace for the next three, until he left for France. He would arrive at her apartment block just before eight and whisk her away to a different venue each night.

That first evening they dined at a quiet little restaurant tucked away in a back street, where the food was
out of this world and the proprietor was fat and jovial,
coming to sit at their table when they had reached the
coffee stage and regaling them with quite horrifying
stories of his youth in Sicily when, it appeared, most of
his contemporaries had been recruited or murdered by
the Mafia. It was blatant fantasy but fascinating none
the less, and they left the restaurant to collapse with
laughter in the dark street outside, feeling that the
evening had been better than a trip to the theatre.

The second evening was spent at an exclusive, top-
class nightclub, where the floor show was riveting and
the food less so. They finished up at a hot-dog stand
just after midnight, eating greasy junk food and sipping
hot tea in elegant evening clothes, much to the
amusement of several down-and-outs who emerged from
cardboard boxes and under newspapers in an alley
leading from the thoroughfare. Jacques treated them all
to food and drink before their taxi driver persuaded them
to leave, clearly feeling he was in danger of being murdered any moment, and they drove away with the smell
of hot-dogs and wildly expensive perfume mingling in
the back of the cab.

Sandi had spent a full week's salary on the fragrant
scent that day in her lunch-hour, but Jacques hadn't even
seemed to notice.

And it was the same story on the third and fourth
night. He entertained her, wined and dined her, laughed
with her and proved himself a captivating and charming
companion, and all the time kept her very firmly at arm's
length. No overtures, no approaches, sexual or
otherwise. Just a friendly kiss goodnight outside her door
when he escorted her back to her apartment and a
cheerful smile of farewell.

And it got to her. It really, really got to her. It was
useless telling herself, night after night in her chaste little

bed, that she wouldn't have it any other way—although logically it was the truth. The fact that he suddenly seemed to view her as something in the region of a cross between a maiden aunt and a sister was aggravating, irksome, hurtful and most of all insulting.

And where was Monique in all this? she asked herself a hundred times a day. Even if he spent some hours in the day with the tall redhead, every minute of his evenings were spent with her, Sandi, and from what she'd seen of Monique it was not the sort of situation the beautiful model would accept without a fight.

What sort of relationship did they have anyway? She didn't understand it. She didn't understand any of it. And the more she tried, the more confused she became. And overall, second by second, minute by minute, hour by hour, her love for him was growing and it terrified her.

She didn't want to love any man, let alone Jacques Challier—a self-confessed cynic of the first order, who regarded women as necessary but expendable pleasure-givers, nice to have around, but for a short time only. Monique was the only one who had lasted the course, and even that was the strangest liaison in history—free love or no free love, she thought miserably.

Every morning she determined in her heart that she would tell him she knew he was here with Monique and ask him exactly how things stood between him and the lovely French girl. And every evening she spoke about a hundred and one topics except the one closest to her heart.

And now it was ten past two on a hot New York afternoon and she was sitting in the airport terminal close to where he would check in, waiting... Waiting for what? she asked herself weakly. To catch him out arriving with Monique? To prove that she wasn't quite the blind, gullible fool he thought she was? To show him she didn't care? He had no idea she would be here—she had led

him to believe she was tied up with an emergency rush
job at work all day—but she had had to come, to see
for herself.

She saw him long before he saw her, his big, broad
body and dark head standing out from the crowd even
in the melting-pot of the air terminal.

'Hello, Jacques.' She had moved swiftly and quietly
to his side and now he swung round to look at her, his
handsome face breaking into one of his rare smiles as
he beamed down at her.

'Sandi?' When, in the next moment, she felt herself
being lifted into the air in a massive bear hug and swung
round before being drawn close to his face as he took
her lips in a scorching kiss, she almost decided to say
nothing. But almost didn't count...

'It's good of you to come and see me off. I didn't
expect you to do that.' He lowered her to her feet as he
spoke, his face warm as his eyes held hers. 'Did you get
finished earlier than you had expected?' he asked
tenderly.

'Finished?' His transparent delight at seeing her there,
the hug, the kiss—this wasn't what she had thought it
would be like, she told herself frantically. And where
was Monique?

'Monique?' She must have spoken the words out loud,
although she hadn't realised she was doing so. 'How on
earth would I know where Monique is?' He looked down
at her in blank surprise.

'But she's here...' She stared up at him, her eyes cloudy
with confusion.

'Is she?' He glanced round the massive terminal filled
with scurrying bodies. 'Where?'

'In New York. Monique is here—but you know that.'
And then, as she saw the black eyes harden and freeze
and a dark mask come down over the autocratic features, she knew. She knew she had just made a terrible
mistake.

'I know that Monique is in New York?' he asked expressionlessly as he bent to pick up the suitcase he had dropped when he had first seen her with one hand, his other holding her arm in a tight grip. 'I think we need to talk, Sandi.'

He led her over to a quiet corner and placed the massive suitcase on the floor before straightening to face her. 'Well, let's have it,' he said tightly. 'Why are you here? And why were you expecting Monique to be around? And, more especially—' and now his eyes chilled into black stone '—why did you come at all if you *did* expect her to be here? I had thought you two hadn't exactly hit it off.'

'I—' She stared up at him as her mind went blank. What could she say? What could she possibly say that wouldn't make it look as though she had been spying on him? Because... And here her face flushed scarlet and her heart began to beat like a tom-tom. Because that was precisely what she had been doing. But she hadn't meant it like that—she hadn't... Had she? She felt the heat rise up into her hair, and still her eyes were glued to his.

'Well?' The word was razor-sharp.

He clearly wasn't going to give any quarter, and she forced herself to answer with all she had... the truth. 'I thought you were here in New York with Monique,' she said flatly, her heart racing. 'On the day you arrived I saw she was working here for a few days and I thought you had come over with her.'

'But I told you I was here on business,' he said grimly.

'I thought you'd combined business with pleasure.'

'Pleasure?' This was getting worse, she thought frantically as his face turned an ugly shade of puce. 'Just a minute; let me get this straight. You thought I had brought Monique over to New York, that I was *with* her in the fullest sense of the word? Is that it?' She nodded miserably. 'And the evenings? When I was with you?

How was this possible?' he asked, his French accent very pronounced as he ground the words out through gritted teeth.

'I thought—' She stopped helplessly. She hadn't thought at all, and the realisation was blinding. She had just allowed all the bitterness from the past to corrode the present. 'I thought you were with her in the day and me in the evenings,' she finished weakly.

'*Zut!*' After the one violent oath he was quiet for a full thirty seconds as he struggled for a self-control that was all but gone.

'Jacques—Jacques, I'm sorry—'

He cut off her apology with a sharp, vicious movement of his hand and she fell silent, looking up at him with huge, luminous eyes.

'So this is the sort of man you think I am?' he asked with a terrible lack of expression in his voice. 'You think I would bring one woman to New York for the week, sleep with her, make sport with her, and then entertain another in the evenings?' It sounded impossible now, when he put it like that, but that was exactly what she had been thinking, and she had no defence against the scathingly fierce anger in his face. 'Answer me, Sandi. Is this what you thought?'

'I suppose so.' She shook her head faintly. 'But—but I wasn't sure—not really—that's why—'

'That is why you came here today,' he finished, his eyes blazing with fury. 'And to think I was pleased to see you, that I thought—' He stopped abruptly. 'What a fool. What a fool I've been.'

'I didn't mean—'

'Do not say another word.' She was frightened now, desperately frightened. She had insulted him, accused him of all manner of crimes and she had been completely wrong.

'Jacques—'

'I mean it, Sandi—not another word or I will not be responsible for my actions.'

'Please listen to me,' she begged brokenly, but his face was as hard as granite, his big body held rigid and taut.

'Like you listened to me?' he asked with a bitter cynicism that smote her heart. 'When I told you about Jacqueline, shared my innermost feelings with you, bared my heart only to have you walk away as though I had just said something obscene? And even then I blamed myself, told myself that I was going too fast for you, that you were not ready to handle anyone else's emotions with your own so raw after your husband's death.

'But it is more than that, isn't it, Sandi? More than your longing for a man who has been dead for three years, more than your unwillingness to step back into the living world again. You do not like me. No—more than that. I do believe you actually hate me.'

'*I don't.*' The words were wrung out of her in a quiet plea but his face didn't change; in fact he took a step back from her, his eyes icy now and full of a pain that she could hardly bear.

'Well, you have come and you have seen,' he said with a dreadful finality. 'You were wrong. But do not let this worry you. There are all manner of diverse crimes of which I have been guilty in the past, and I am sure you can dig those up if you really try. No doubt there will be more in the future too. As I have said before, I am not a saint. I never have been and I am not sure I ever could be. There, you have it. I confess.'

He was furiously, viciously, blazingly mad, and she knew her legs wouldn't hold her much longer against the force of his rage. 'But this need not concern you, need it?' he went on. 'As you have said, I am merely Ann's brother-in-law—a relation to her only through marriage and nothing to you. We need not even meet again. I will make sure that when you visit France to see your sister I am not present. Does this suit you?'

'No—' She wanted to reach out to him but she really wasn't sure that he wouldn't knock her hands away, so great was his rage. 'I don't want that, believe me, Jacques. Let me explain—'

'But I—I want that,' he said proudly, his face closed against her. 'Goodbye, Sandi.'

She wanted to scream and shout and cry, to run after him, throw herself in front of him, grovel at his feet—anything to make him understand.

But she did none of those things as he walked away. She had thought she had been through the worst that could happen to her when she had found out about Ian, but that was nothing, nothing to this pain that was tearing her apart now.

If she had loved Ian, or the man she had thought he was, it had been but a pale reflection of the emotion she felt for Jacques Challier. He was her heart, her blood, her life, and she felt that he was taking all those things as she watched him disappear into the crowd without a backward turn of his proud head. And she had been responsible for this. It was all her fault, all of it. She wouldn't be able to bear it...

She gave a convulsive groan, careless of the glances around her, and stumbled to the ladies' cloakroom where she locked herself in the loo for a long time—how long she never did remember. She sat in a frozen state of stunned misery, hearing the excited laughter of children, the grumblings of over-stressed mothers, the wails of babies being changed, the giggling of animated teenagers—all the things that made up the flow of humanity—as she went over and over their conversation in her mind. On and on, relentlessly torturing herself, until she felt as if her heart had been ripped out at the roots.

And no matter how she thought of it, how she tried to justify herself, to bring some excuses to bear, there simply were no excuses. He would never forgive her. That knowledge was seared into the whole of her body. Never.

Eventually she left the tiny, safe little box, walking like an old woman to the car park and finding her car among the myriad of others, and it wasn't until she was in the driving seat, travelling far too fast along the freeway, that she asked herself how she was going to get through the rest of her life.

CHAPTER NINE

'SANDI?' Arianne's voice was anxious but excited. 'Thank goodness I have reached you. I tried to contact you at your office, but they told me you had left for home.'

'Ann?' Sandi's stomach had just turned over.

'The baby is on the way. Claude and I have just brought her into the hospital—'

'But it's early,' Sandi protested weakly. 'A month early. Is anything wrong?'

'No, no; please do not distress yourself. Everything is fine.' But the other woman's voice, in spite of its attempt at cheerfulness, was not totally reassuring.

'Has she definitely started?' Sandi asked quickly. 'I mean—'

'The waters have broken.' Arianne's voice was quiet now. 'There is no doubt that the baby will be born some time soon. Once the waters have broken the risk of infection is too high for her to be left.'

'Is she having any pains?' Sandi asked numbly.

'A little, just a little. Would you like me to ring you in an hour or so, when I know a little more? The doctors are with her now—'

'No. I'm coming over.' Sandi sat down with a little plop on the chair near the phone as her legs gave way. 'I'll be there as soon as I can—I'll ring the airport now. If I'm delayed in any way I'll phone you at the hospital. You will stay with her?' she asked anxiously.

'Of course, Sandi. Do not worry,' Arianne said swiftly. 'She is our daughter now, and this is Emile's child. We

158

will look after her as you would until you get here. She is perfectly safe.'

'Thank you, Arianne. I'll be there as soon as I can. Give my love to Ann.'

She put down the phone and stared at it in stunned shock for a moment before grabbing it again and dialling the number of the airport with shaking fingers. Incredibly, miraculously, they had a cancellation on a flight leaving for France that night, although she would be hard-pressed to make the airport in time. She rang for a taxi-cab before throwing some things into a case and phoning Andy with a list of hasty instructions, and then left the house within ten minutes of receiving Arianne's call.

Through the mad dash to the airport and the race to get on the plane she had no time to think, but once settled in the massive aircraft with all the panic behind her her thoughts were all of Ann—Ann and a certain tall, dark Frenchman who had vowed never to set eyes on her again.

The weeks since Jacques had left had been horrendous. For the first few days she had moved from one day to the next in a state of suspended animation, her mind stunned and frozen by the enormity of their confrontation. And then the wound had begun to bleed, slowly at first, before opening up into a gushing flood that had had her walking the flat at night until the early hours, quite literally holding her head in her hands as she had moaned her anguish out loud.

The knowledge that she had destroyed anything they might have had, completely and irrevocably, was unbearable. The fact that he hadn't been in America with Monique must have meant that he had come to see *her*. That was the thought that was driving her mad. And now she had lost the chance to be even on the perimeter of his life through fear—fear and cowardice. Fear that history would repeat itself and he would leave her, like

Ian, and cowardice in that she hadn't opened her eyes
to see him, the real Jacques Challier, without the spectre
of Ian sitting on his shoulder. In that, she hadn't given
them a chance.

But she had to concentrate on Ann now. As the plane
rose majestically into the air with a slow whoosh she
willed her sister to feel her love over the thousands of
miles separating them.

This baby meant more than it would ever know. It
had pulled its mother from the brink of the abyss Ann
had glimpsed when Emile had been killed, had forged
a link of steel wrapped in a silken thread with its father's
estranged family and provided Ann with loving, doting
in-laws and other relations, including Odile and her
children, whom Ann spoke of often in her telephone calls
and letters. Nothing must happen to this baby; it was
too precious, too cherished, too loved.

For the whole of the seven-hour journey Sandi sent
her prayers heavenward, unable to sleep or even doze in
spite of the endless nights of cat-naps she had endured
for the last few weeks.

When she arrived in France she felt like a wet rag,
and a great sense of despondency and foreboding kept
her silent and tense on the long drive from the airport
to the hospital, which was situated several miles from
the Challier château.

The July morning was already wide awake and one
of glorious sunshine, although it was still only seven
o'clock, but as the taxi ate up the miles Sandi didn't
notice the scenery outside the windows. Her whole self,
her very being was homed in on Ann and the tiny infant
who was being born a month too soon. She told herself
over and over again that that was nothing these days.
They were saving babies at twenty-six weeks now—
twenty-four even—modern technology was wonderful... But it didn't help. Nothing helped. She just
wanted to get to her sister's side.

As the taxi drew up outside the hospital her stomach muscles clenched in a giant knot. Jacques had told her that the small private hospital was second to none, beautifully and expertly equipped, with the added advantage of boasting the finest obstetrician in all of France on its board. She hoped that consultant had been with her sister during the night—oh, she did.

As the taxi driver hauled her suitcase out of the boot she opened her bag to sort out the fare, whereupon a large male hand was placed on top of hers. 'Do not worry, Sandi; I will see to this.' She smiled up at Claude Challier, touched that he must have been looking out for her. 'Go now—go and see Ann.'

'Is she—?' Her voice faltered; his face was giving nothing away. 'She's all right?'

'I'm under orders to say nothing, but I can tell you she is well—very well.' He beamed at her, and for a moment he looked so like Jacques when he had first seen her that fateful day at the airport that she felt her face freeze. 'Go on. It is straight through the front doors, down the hall, first left and the room number is four.'

He gave her a little push as she stood transfixed, and then she was hurrying into the plush interior of the building where the perfume of flowers and thick, soft carpets competed with the faint but unmistakable smell of antiseptic and things medical.

'Ann?' She had entered the room on a little rush of excitement and anticipation before realising that her sister might be asleep, but Ann wasn't asleep. She was sitting bolt upright in bed, her eyes on the door and her arms cradling a very small bundle swathed in a lacy blanket.

'Sandi—oh, Sandi. I've been dying for you to get here...' As her sister's eyes filled with tears so did Sandi's, and the two smiled shakily as Sandi sat carefully on the bed before giving Ann a fierce hug. 'Here, say hello to your niece.'

'A little girl?' Sandi gazed wonderingly at the minute crumpled face topped with a smudge of wispy black hair, at the tiny eyelids closed tight and the diminutive little hand resting against one cheek. 'Oh, Ann, she's so small.'

'She isn't that small!' There was a wealth of feeling in Ann's voice. 'She weighed in at a full eight pounds, and that was more than enough, I can tell you! If she'd waited another month she'd have been stuck in there for ever.'

'Was it awful?'

'Bad enough.' Ann grimaced feelingly. 'But Arianne was wonderful. She was born at five this morning and Arianne stayed with me the whole time. She's just gone to organise some breakfast for you, but I think it was really to let us have a few minutes alone.'

'What are you going to call her?' Sandi asked as Ann placed the tiny infant carefully in her arms. The baby felt warm and smelt wonderful—a mixture of baby powder and something indefinable that brought a choking feeling to Sandi's throat. She was so beautiful and so tiny and— And she would never have one. She pushed the thought back into the recesses of her mind and concentrated on Ann fiercely.

'Emily.' Ann's mouth quivered, and Sandi reached out one arm to hug her close again. 'It's as near to Emile as I can get.'

By the time Arianne and Claude arrived ten minutes later, bearing a large tray for Sandi, both sisters' emotions were under control, although their eyes were pink-rimmed. The four of them were sitting chatting, Emily still fast asleep but now cocooned in a neat little glass crib at the side of the bed, when a knock at the door caused Ann to call out an immediate 'come in'. And Jacques came in.

Sandi's heart stopped for a moment, and then ran on at a speed the rest of her body couldn't keep up with. She felt faint, giddy, and for a second really felt as if she might pass out, but the fact that when she looked into his face the dark, glittering eyes stared straight through her put iron in her backbone and brought an upward tilt to her chin. She took a long sip of the hot coffee she was finishing, stitched a polite smile on her face and said nothing.

'Where is this new arrival?' Jacques's eyes were soft as he glanced at Ann, who was trying not to look overly proud. 'May I see her?'

'Of course.' Ann gestured to the crib and right on cue, as Jacques bent over her, Emily opened her eyes and yawned. 'Pick her up,' Ann encouraged. 'It's all right.'

The sight of him cradling the small infant was almost too much for Sandi, and the lump in her throat threatened to explode in an avalanche of tears, but she excused herself quickly, after they had exchanged a brief nod and polite greeting for the sake of the others, on the pretext that she needed the bathroom. And when she returned ten minutes later, the armour of self-control firmly in place, he had gone.

All that day and the next, when Ann returned home to the château with Emily, she expected him to call—if only to exercise his right to ignore her as he had done to such good effect at the hospital. But by the end of the second day she realised he wasn't going to come. She didn't exist for him any more. And with that knowledge a rage came, and with that rage pride, and a painful dignity that she hugged to her like an all-enveloping cloak.

He was just like Ian. He hadn't really cared. He had wanted her for a brief sexual fling, nothing more, otherwise he wouldn't have been able to dismiss her with such coldness, without letting her explain. And she hated him. Loathed, detested and hated him. Ian had wanted only her money; Jacques had wanted only her body. And of the two she felt that Ian had served her least harshly.

The next morning she booked her return flight to New York, happy in the knowledge that she was leaving Ann and the baby in good hands. The Challiers, all of them, were clearly over the moon with their new family member, and the fact that she wasn't a boy was clearly as unimportant to them as to the proud mother. They loved Emily because she was part of Ann and part of Emile, and Ann was blooming under their devotion.

'You're leaving us tomorrow, Sandi?' They had all just finished dinner and had retired to the magnificent drawing room for coffee as the dusky evening sent the scents of summer through the open windows, the last of the dying sunlight falling in stark beams across the room. 'You are welcome to stay longer.'

'I know that.' She smiled at Claude. 'But I've had quite a lot of time off recently, and my company has been very good about it. I don't feel—'

When, in the next instant, the door to the drawing room was flung aside rather than opened, Arianne actually gave a little squeal of alarm before she saw her son framed in the doorway. *'Oh, mon Dieu!* Jacques, what on earth do you think you are doing, frightening us all like that? What is wrong?'

And for the first time in his life Jacques Challier neglected the lessons of his privileged childhood, the conventions, the polite propriety, the decorous good manners that were as much a part of him as breathing, and walked over to stand in front of Sandi without looking to left or right, his eyes blazing. 'You were going to leave? Tomorrow? Early in the morning? Without telling me?'

'I—' Her hand was at her throat as she struggled to make sense of what he was saying. 'I—'

'How dare you? How *dare* you think you could do this?'

'Jacques—?' As Claude rose to his feet, his eyes flying between Sandi's shocked white face and Jacques's countenance, which was as dark as midnight, he put out a hand to his son, only to remove it a second later as Jacques turned to look at him, his eyes blazing.

'Do not interfere, Papa. This is between Sandi and me.' He swung back to face her, his eyes narrowed. 'Well? You are going to leave tomorrow?'

'Yes.' She stood up now, her face pale, but her own fury at his arrogance burned in two bright spots on her cheeks. 'And why shouldn't I? You haven't called round or phoned—'

'How could I, when I was in Paris?' he snarled ferociously. 'You could have phoned me—I gave you the number.'

'The number?' She stared at him blankly, and at the look on her face he swung round to Arianne, who had just uttered a soft cry of dismay.

'You gave Sandi the letter?' he asked swiftly.

'Oh, Jacques, I am so sorry, but with the baby... I forgot. I still have it in my handbag.' Arianne was clearly horrified.

'C'est impossible!' He turned back to Sandi, his voice just a tone or so quieter. 'I gave my mother a letter to give you that day at the hospital. I had to go to Paris; there was no way I could get out of it. The letter explained it all.'

'I am so sorry.' Arianne's voice was tragic, but Jacques ignored them all now, reaching out and taking Sandi's arm then practically frogmarching her across the room.

'You are coming with me. I will have no more of this— this *ridiculous* situation,' he snarled softly. 'You did not receive the letter but you clearly made no enquiries about me, asked nothing about where I was, what was happening. You were just going to disappear again, weren't you? *Weren't you?*'

'*Again?*' Her voice was so shrill that Emily, asleep in her frothy pink crib in the corner of the room, wailed with shock. 'It was you who left me, remember? You wouldn't let me explain, tell you—'

'Sandi?' Ann's voice was utterly bewildered, and as they turned to face the rest of the room from the doorway, Jacques's hand still tight on her arm, Sandi saw the look of almost comical amazement that was on her sister's face mirrored in the expressions of the others. 'You've been seeing Jacques?' It said a lot for Ann's state of concern that she hadn't sprung to her newborn offspring at the first cry. 'Without telling me?'

'I haven't been seeing him,' Sandi said quickly. 'It isn't like that—'

'The hell it isn't!' Jacques glared at the rest of the room as he pushed Sandi through the doorway. 'Sandi is staying with me tonight. That is all any of you need to know. And whether she will be returning to America tomorrow is doubtful, so I would suggest one of you rings the airline and tells them—'

'You'd better not! I'm going back...' As Ann and Arianne and Claude heard the sound of Sandi's voice fade away and the front door bang shut Odile and André rushed into the room, their faces full of alarm.

'What on earth is happening?' André glanced over to where Ann had lifted Emily from the crib and was rocking her in her arms soothingly, murmuring a host of nothings as she did so. 'I thought something was wrong with the child.'

'Emily's fine.' They all turned to look at Ann, and as Arianne absorbed the look in her daughter-in-law's eyes she smiled slowly. 'And I think perhaps now Sandi is going to be fine,' Ann went on. 'I should have guessed, noticed...'

'Well, I didn't and I am his mother,' Arianne said quietly.

'Would someone please tell me what is going on?' Claude stared from one to the other and shook his head slowly. 'I am fast losing my grasp of what is real and what is not. And please, I do not wish anyone to say anyone else is fine, all right?'

But Sandi felt far from fine as she sat beside Jacques in the silver beast of a car. That he was blazingly, furiously angry was obvious, but what was really terrifying was the emotion that was running through her veins now. Because the temptation to say, to do anything she could to make everything all right was painfully strong, but even stronger was the knowledge that it scared her half to death that he had come for her like this.

It spoke of something more than mere bodily desire, and in spite of all her ragings, all her accusations, spoken and unspoken, the thought that she might be able to trust him, be able to reach out to him, the thought that there might be something between them, was too frightening to contemplate. She loved him, there was no doubt about that, she thought silently, but she didn't trust him. She doubted if she could ever trust any man again.

When he had, as she had mistakenly thought, flaunted Monique in front of her eyes, a tiny part of her, unacknowledged until this precise moment of time, had been relieved. It had been an escape route, an excuse to keep that secret place at the very depth of her hidden, and, yes, she had been relieved. She couldn't face the thought of opening up, of committing herself again, only to be ripped apart. She really couldn't.

'Where are we going?' she asked in a very small voice when the electric atmosphere in the car became unbearable.

'You know exactly where we are going,' Jacques said tightly without glancing at her. 'To my home.'

'You can't do this—'

'I just have.' Now he did spare her a swift glance, and she shivered at the burning intensity in the dark eyes. 'I have made myself the fool for you. Now are you satisfied?'

'Please don't say that.' She had made up her mind three years ago as to the route her life would take, and it didn't include a tall, dark, handsome Frenchman who would always have women flocking round him like flies. She couldn't, she just couldn't handle this, whether he wanted her for one night, one month, one year...

'Why not? I have never been afraid of the truth. You know I care for you, and you are attracted to me in spite of this obsession you have with your late husband.'

'I do *not* have an obsession with Ian.' Well, perhaps she did, she thought miserably. But certainly not in the way Jacques meant. 'You don't understand.'

'Because you will not let me understand.' It was so near the truth that she couldn't answer him. 'I was mad at you in America; I will not deny it. When you told me what you had suspected all that time you had been with me—' He stopped abruptly and drew a harsh, ragged breath through his teeth. 'I could have throttled you there and then, especially as I had told you things I had never told a living soul—about Jacqueline, about the way I felt.

'I had been miserable since you had left France, had engineered a visit to America purely to spend some time with you, and I felt you had betrayed me in some way. That may not be so, but that is the way I felt. But once I was home I began to see that I had tried to rush you again, to force the issue, and we had been doing so well. You enjoyed our evenings in New York?' he asked softly.

'You know I did.' And she had, so much.

'And I was most restrained, was I not? The polite goodnight kisses, the no touching? I could not believe that this was the Jacques Challier that had been in my skin for thirty-six years!' The self-mockery was soft but with a cutting edge that told her he had found the going really tough. 'So I decided that what had been accomplished once could be accomplished again, in time. I could be patient—hell, I had no choice. I would wait until you came over to see Ann and then I would continue the softly-softly approach until I had won. It was simple.'

'Jacques—'

'But you, you are not simple.' He glared at her now. 'What is it about me that you hate so much?'

'I don't hate you,' she said flatly, her heart thudding.

'You treat the people you *like* this way?'

She was saved the necessity of a reply to the sarcastic taunt as the beautiful car nosed carefully into Jacques's courtyard. As before the geese put up a show of cackling displeasure at having their quiet serenity interrupted, before retiring, feathers ruffled, to a far corner, from where they glanced balefully over their shoulders as Jacques led the way into the house.

'I want to go back, Jacques.'

'No way.' He turned in the middle of the sitting room and shook his head slowly as he let his eyes run over her slender shape. 'And you've lost weight.' He moved swiftly to her side and looked down at her intently. 'Why have you lost weight? You were too thin to start with.'

'Thank you *very* much.' The criticism took care of the weak tears that had been in danger of falling as she had glanced round the lovely farmhouse she had never expected to see again. 'And you—you're perfect, I suppose?'

'As near as damn it.' He smiled, but she just couldn't smile back.

'You were horrible at the hospital the morning Emily was born,' she said flatly. 'Absolutely horrible.'

'I was petrified,' he said soberly, shaking his head slowly as her eyes flew to his. 'You find this hard to accept? You think I am a man of stone, is that it? Well, I can assure you I was scared to death when I walked in that room, Sandi. Part of me wanted to ignore everyone else and take you in my arms and force you—*force* you to care for me. Another part, the sensible part, was telling me I had to follow the route I had planned and play it cool and slow. Another—'

He raked back his hair abruptly. 'Oh, hell, I could go on all night but that will not help us now. For once in my life I was out of my depth and unsure how to handle things—you... I was supposed to be in Paris mid-morning and it was an appointment I could not miss, one of vital importance. I put the number of my hotel in the letter and asked you to ring me.'

'I didn't know.'

'Would you have rung if you had?' he asked quietly as he looked her square in the eye. 'Would you, Sandi?'

'I don't know...' She broke the contact and sank down onto one of the big easy chairs, shaking her head helplessly. 'I thought—'

'I know what you thought,' he said tightly as he continued looking down at her bent head, her hair shining like liquid gold in the dim light of the wall lamps dotted about the large room. 'You made it absolutely clear on the morning I left New York what sort of man you thought I was, but I hoped that the realisation that you were wrong about Monique would perhaps allow you to consider that you might be wrong about everything else as well.

'Monique is a beautiful, sensual woman—' her eyes shot to his face as he spoke the redhead's name '—and utterly spoilt, vain, irritating, egotistical, shallow... Need I go on?' he asked sardonically.

'But you were so friendly with her,' she protested faintly.

'Sandi, she is the daughter of my parents' best friends,' he answered patiently. 'What did you expect me to do? Spit in her eye? Her mother has been trying to engineer some sort of match between Monique and me for years, but Monique knows full well how I view that. I frequently put her in her place—she needs someone to keep her in order—but that is as far as it goes.'

And that would make him even more of a challenge to Monique, Sandi thought with sudden intuition. The beautiful model was used to having men fall at her feet; the fact that this one was immune to her charms would drive her crazy.

'Have you ever—ever taken her out?' she asked tentatively, not really wishing to know the answer but having to ask anyway.

'A few times, when she was younger and a slightly more mellow character,' he answered, with an offhandedness that told her there was no involvement on his side at least. 'Parties of joint friends, that sort of thing, but only on a friendship basis. I have never enjoyed her company.'

He looked her straight in the eye now as he dropped on his heels to crouch in front of her. 'That is the truth, Sandi. There has never ever been any sort of relationship between us beyond one of platonic friendship. I know Monique's type. The world is full of beautiful, spoilt women who think the sun and moon revolve around them alone. I have not been an angel, but you know this already; I have not tried to pretend otherwise. But Monique? No. Nothing like that was ever on the cards and she knows it.'

'I see.' She stared at his dark face so close to hers and her heart went haywire. She believed him, and she knew now that Jacques was not the sort of man to be involved with more than one woman at a time, but... There was no way she could be that woman. She couldn't handle being just one in a long stream of affairs. Eventually he would tire of her—his sort of man always did—and then—

'"I see"? Is that it?' She was unaware that the play of emotions over her face had caught at him with knifelike pain. 'This does not affect you in any way?'

'Jacques—'

'No—no more "Jacques, this", "Jacques, that",' he said abruptly as he rose again to stare down at her with flashing black eyes. 'You always speak my name like that when you are withdrawing a little, doing this thing you do so well of shutting me out. I expected too much when I told you of Jacqueline, I know that. I felt I was giving you privileged information, which was unquestionably a great presumption on my part.

'You did not ask to be told, I decided to tell you— and the fact that it did not make any difference to the way you looked at me was not your fault. I should not have expected this. I acted like a spoilt child and was so concerned with *my* feelings, the way I felt you had rejected me when I had honoured you so mightily—' his voice was dripping with self-contempt and self-mockery '—that I did not consider you at all. In this I was wrong, I admit it, but I will not let you shut me out any longer, Sandi, whether you like it or not. You are attracted to me, I know this, and that is a start.'

'I can't let myself be attracted to you. I'm sorry,' she said miserably.

'You can.' He eyed her hotly. 'However much you loved your husband, however much you miss him, he is not here and I am.'

His words were meant to be brutal, to shock her out of the brokenness he felt she was feeling, but they got no reaction and it puzzled him.

'I love you, Sandi.' The words were torn out of him and brought her eyes to his. 'I've fought against it, railed against it, told myself I was foolish to ever get emotionally involved with another woman after Jacqueline. But this is not a mind thing, it is a thing of the heart, and I have no defence against it. I did not intend to tell you, but I must. And I will not let you bury yourself, spirit, mind and body, in the way you have done for three years. You might never feel the same about me as I feel for you, but at least I can make you start living again.'

This was killing her. He didn't know it, but he was killing her, she thought blindly. The final nail in the coffin. He had just destroyed the last defence she'd had with three simple little words. 'I love you'. 'Don't say these things, Jacques—'

'Why? Because you do not feel they are the truth?' he asked softly. 'Is that it? But I do love you, Sandi. I am helpless before this feeling I have for you. It makes me vulnerable, exposed, wide open, and I do not like this but I can do nothing about it. I did not love Jacqueline like this and I shall not love again like it. You are the love of my life—'

'No!' Her voice was an agonised cry against herself. She was being offered heaven and she didn't have the courage to take it. She couldn't—she *couldn't* do what he had done and open herself so completely to another human being again.

'I want to marry you, Sandi, to commit myself to you,' he went on relentlessly, sensing that some sort of break-through was near. 'I want to share my days and my nights with you, to have children that are a part of me and a part of you—'

'I will never marry again.' She shrank inwardly, her stomach shrivelling into a tiny, tight ball. 'Never.'

'You loved him that much?' And it was the pain in his voice that broke the dam.

'*Loved* him? I hated him, loathed him,' she said as she closed her eyes against his face, her voice quivering with anguish. 'He was a monster from hell.' And she began to talk, to tell him all of it, with her eyes tightly shut and her voice so full of pain and agony and humiliation that Jacques's face was wet when he suddenly took her in his arms, pulling her against him with a fierceness that stopped her words and her breath.

'No.' She freed herself with a quiet firmness that stopped him more effectively than any demented struggling would have done. 'You must hear it all.' And he did, every last word, until all she had said was branded on his mind and he would have given the world, all he possessed, for one minute with the man who had caused her such pain.

'And I love you, Jacques. I want you to know that now.' It was said with such flatness, such a strange lack of emotion that it stopped him from the reaction the words would have caused minutes ago. 'I never really loved Ian—I didn't even know the real man at all—but I do love you. And because I love you—' she raised her eyes to his now '—I want you to forget me, to find someone else who can be what you want her to be.'

Jacques had thought that he had been through every emotion known to man in the last ten minutes, but now he felt a new one, compounded of fury and resentment and sheer anger that she could speak in such a way after what they had just shared. He didn't move, and her words hung like something unclean in the stark silence that followed, filled with their own vibrating energy which pounded against his eardrums with a force that was unbearable.

And as she looked into his face she saw a stranger metamorphose in front of her—a dangerously angry, blazingly mad stranger, with eyes that were fire and a mouth that was a straight line in the hardness of his face.

'How dare you? How dare you say I should find someone else?' he ground out slowly through clenched teeth, and she backed away from him until she was standing against the wall. 'What do you think this emotion is that I feel for you? Something that can be turned off and on like a tap? I love you, dammit. I want to marry you; I want to have children; I want you to be their mother.

'I cannot change what Ian has done, heal the scars you bear in your head from his treatment of you; all I can promise you is that I will not be the same. That I will love you, cherish you, protect you all the days of my life. Do you believe this, Sandi? Do you?'

She felt paralysed by the raw emotion in his face and voice, unable to move, to make any response.

'Do you, Sandi?' His voice was softer now, calmer, but with a terrible determination to wring an answer out of her. 'Do you believe in my love, believe you can trust me?'

'No. . .' Her reply was a long scream of anguish and pain and loss. 'I can't. I can't—don't you see? I can't say that when it isn't true. I don't know if I'll ever be able to say it! *I don't! I don't!* I can't be what you want me to be; it's too late for that. I want to trust you, to believe we'd always be together, but I can't—I can't feel it in here.' She pounded her chest with her fists until he caught her hands in his, drawing her against him as he slowly stroked her hair with cool, firm fingers, his voice soothing and calm.

'Enough, little one, enough. You are making yourself ill and I do not wish this. You are too tired to talk any more—enough, now. No more crying.' She hadn't realised she was weeping until he had spoken, but now she became aware of the tears flooding down her face, and when he gathered her in his arms and began to walk up the winding staircase she was too tired to resist, her head falling against the hard wall of his chest as she relaxed against the male warmth of him.

She didn't want to lose him. The thought was all around her as he walked with her into a pretty bedroom and laid her gently on the big four-poster, his eyes soft. She didn't want to lose him but she would. She had to. But they could have one night together—surely one night wasn't too much to ask to last her a lifetime? When he went to turn and leave she caught at his hand, her voice still trembling from the force of her weeping.

'Don't go, Jacques. Please don't go.'

'It is all right. Everything will be all right.' He was quick to reassure her as he sat on the side of the bed, stroking her hair back from her damp face, but she didn't want this fatherly care; she wanted—she wanted him. She needed him. Just once, that was all she would ask.

'Make love to me.'

'What?' His hand stilled on her forehead, his eyes wide with surprise.

'I want you, Jacques.' She reached up to him, drawing his head down to hers before he could reply and pressing her mouth against his as she quivered against him. 'I love you. I do...'

For a moment she thought he was going to resist her, and then he responded with a fierce, desperate urgency that had her moaning against his lips as his hands explored her body. Their kissing, their touching was frantic and fierce, and she was lost in the mounting whirlpool that was carrying her to its core, hardly aware that he had removed her blouse until she felt his lips burning on her bare skin, creating fire wherever they lingered.

He was lying next to her now, as he kissed and stroked her, the little words of endearment and love that he whispered against her skin adding to the entrancing magic of his intoxicating lovemaking. She felt a tenderness that she'd never known before blossom into being as she saw his dark head against the pale skin of her breasts, and then a languorous, burning warmth began to seep into every part of her and she began to tremble helplessly, her body shaking against his. As his mouth found hers again she kissed him back wildly, wantonly, until they were both trembling, his body rock-hard and fierce against hers and his eyes narrowed slits of black light.

'You're wonderful, incredible... You see how it will be for us...?' He was on the edge of losing control, she knew it, and she wanted him to take her—wanted to be as one with him for one glorious night.

'I love you...' She murmured his name as he kissed her bare flesh hungrily. 'I want to be able to remember this all my life...' And the moment she had spoken, the second the words had left her lips, she felt him freeze against her, his mouth still on the warm swell of her breasts for a timeless second before he raised his head slowly, his eyes seeking her face.

'All your life?' He raised himself on one elbow, his body still shaking from the force of his desire but his control rigid. 'Why all your life, Sandi? There will be many more nights, days, shared between us, because I intend to live a long, long time.'

And then she realised he had misunderstood when she had reached for him, asked for his love. He had thought...

What he had thought was blazing in his eyes now, his mouth hard as he rose from the bed to look down at her from his great height. 'You thought I would be content with one taste of you? That I would give you a parting gift—something like that?' His voice was very tight now, very controlled.

'Oh, no, Sandi; get that out of your head. I am going to have you, all of you—heart, soul and body; you can get used to that idea right now. I don't care how long I have to wait but you will be mine, and with a gold band on the third finger of your left hand too. You are not some cheap affair, some liaison that I can walk away from with nothing more than a warm memory, and I will not be that for you. I will not allow it. You will not reduce us to that. Now, go to sleep.'

He wasn't going to leave her? To calmly walk out and leave her? 'Jacques—'

'I said go to sleep, Sandi.'

'I shall be leaving in the morning.' The words were both a plea and a warning, and his face closed still more as he looked at her from the open doorway. 'I mean it, Jacques. I'm going back to New York, to the life I have chosen. It's the only thing I can do—you must see that. I wouldn't be any good for you—I would destroy anything we might have—'

'Have you finished?' His voice was cold now, cold and remote, and she sat up jerkily on the bed and pulled her clothing around her, her face flushed and embarrassed at the state of her undress.

'Yes, I've finished,' she said dully, and she had. She could never be the kind of wife he wanted, the kind of wife she would have given the world to be. How could she be when the very basis of her love for him had the element of trust missing? It would be like a canker, eating into both of them until it ended in heartbreak and confusion and pain.

And she wouldn't pretend—couldn't. He deserved the best and she wasn't the best; it was as simple as that. Something had been torn out of her when Ian had betrayed her, something soft and vital and warm and magical. It had gone, and although she had searched for it—more and more over the last few weeks—it still eluded her. She couldn't trust him.

'Goodnight, Sandi.'

The door closed behind him and she sank back against the pillows of the big bed, aware that she was shivering uncontrollably. It was the end. Tomorrow she would walk out of his life for ever. *It had to be this way.*

CHAPTER TEN

'I UNDERSTAND your flight is at midday?'

She had heard the telephone ring last night, just after Jacques had left her room, but had been unable to determine who was calling even though she had crept to the door of her room and listened to his voice filtering up from the hall.

'Yes.' She glanced at him now as they sat on the patio, which had already been warmed by the early morning sun, having a breakfast of fruit and toast. At first she had felt she couldn't eat a thing, but then, at the sight of him digging in with gusto, pride had come to her rescue, and she had managed an adequate, if small, breakfast. 'But I need to get back to the château in time to pack and say goodbye to everyone.'

'This is understood.'

She didn't understand him this morning—she really didn't, she thought wearily as she lay back against her chair and pretended to enjoy the remainder of her coffee.

'There are a couple of calls I have to make and then we can leave,' he said coolly, rising to his feet. 'You will wait here?'

'Yes.' Her voice was lethargic, dull, but that was how she felt inside. She hadn't slept for more than half an hour during the night, and that had only been as dawn was breaking. She felt tired, crumpled and a mess without her make-up or even her lipstick.

The bathroom *en suite* had provided shampoo, soap and the basic necessities, including a small comb that had proved painful when she'd tried to untangle her thick curls, but she knew her eyes were swollen and pink-rimmed and her face was pale and washed out. Still, perhaps it was for the best that she would walk out of

179

his life looking like something the cat had dragged in,
she thought painfully. No false illusions about looking
radiant in the morning, anyway!

Jacques, on the other hand, had looked the picture
of health as he sat at the table when she had tentatively
made an appearance downstairs. Freshly shaved, black
curls slicked back but already beginning to flop across
his forehead, eyes bright and hard mouth smiling. She
could have hit him. And kissed him. And—

Stop it, stop it, she told herself firmly as her heart
began to thud and pound at the thought that she would
never see him again. She mustn't think, mustn't feel.
She just had to get through this day the best she could
and then take stock. Of what, she didn't know. The rest
of her life stretched out in front of her like an endless
nightmare. If only he hadn't told her he loved her, that
he wanted to marry her, she could have tried to pretend
it was just a thing of the flesh and maybe got by. But
now—

'Oh, God, help me.' She actually said the prayer out
loud, her eyes desperate. She had to be strong for a few
more hours at least. She couldn't ruin his life as well as
her own.

'OK.' He appeared in the doorway, smiling again, as
though he hadn't a care in the world. 'We are ready to
leave, yes?'

'Yes.' She stood up abruptly, her dignity gathered
round her like a cloak, and marched past him with her
head held high. His eyes were soft on the back of her
head as she walked out to the car, but once he had opened
the door and settled her inside the same remote, cool
mask he had worn all morning was firmly in place.

She sat in numb misery for the first half an hour, utterly lost in her own pain. He had given up. Well, she
was glad, *glad*. Of course she was. She just wished he
hadn't done it so quickly and apparently with such ease,
that was all. She shut her eyes at the unfairness of her
thoughts. What was the matter with her? The man had

offered to marry her and she had refused—several times.
What had she expected anyway? He had said once before
that he wasn't the type of man to bang his head against
a brick wall, and she couldn't blame him.

'Jacques?' Another half an hour had gone by and, as
once before, when he had taken her to his home instead
of the château, she felt that something was wrong.
'Where are we?'

'Where are we?' He gave her one lightning glance and
she knew immediately that she was right: they weren't
going to the château. She glanced anxiously out of the
window now, before swinging her head back to his dark
profile.

'Yes, where are we?' she asked shrilly. 'This isn't the
way back.'

'It is the way back to where I want to go,' he said
smoothly, his voice silky and soft. 'We are heading for
Soane et Loire; does that help?'

'Of course it doesn't help,' she said tightly. 'Because
you know full well I haven't the faintest idea where that
is.'

'It is in Burgundy.' His tone was helpful. 'OK?'

No, it is not OK.' She couldn't believe it; she just
couldn't believe it—it was in quite the wrong direction.
'What about my plane?'

'What plane?' he asked innocently.

'The one I am supposed to catch today.' Driver or no
driver, she was going to hit him in a minute, she thought
hotly.

'I told Ann to cancel that when she rang last night,'
he said coolly, his voice bland. 'At the same time I arranged for your suitcase to be delivered to my home just
after breakfast. I thought it would spoil our time together
if you weren't able to feel comfortable in your own
things—'

'Our time together?' She had given up trying not to
shriek, and he closed his eyes for the briefest moment
as the sound reverberated round the car.

'That is most unattractive, you know that, don't you?'

She answered him with a most unladylike oath that caused him to tut-tut deep in his throat. 'You can't—' She stopped abruptly. 'This is crazy, Jacques. What are you going to do? Keep me prisoner somewhere until you get your own way?'

'Exactly.' And now there was no amusement or mockery in the swift glance that burnt across her stunned face. 'For as long as it takes, my love.'

'I don't believe this.' She shut her own eyes now, leaning back against the seat helplessly. 'I just don't believe this is happening to me.' He said nothing, concentrating on the road with just a narrowing of his eyes against the brilliant sunlight outside the powerful car. 'What's at Soane et Loire anyway?' she asked after a few electric moments had ticked away.

'Lunch.' The deep voice was unforgivably unconcerned.

'Lunch?' She sat bolt upright again. 'Then where is it we're going? What's our final destination?'

'My family's little log cabin in the mountains,' he said calmly. 'That's where we were when Emile—' He stopped abruptly. 'That is our hideaway, our retreat,' he continued smoothly after a few seconds had passed. 'No telephone, no TV—heaven...'

'And where, exactly, is heaven situated?' she asked with enormous self-control as she forced her voice a few tones lower than it wanted to be.

'Savoie, in the French Alps.'

She shut her eyes and said nothing. There was nothing to say, after all.

They lunched at a charming hotel built next to a Romanesque church with a wonderful backdrop of mountains and forest behind, and an enchanting vista of deep valleys with colourful meadows from the dining room. The steak *au poivre* melted in the mouth, and the *ananas au kirsch*—fresh pineapple chunks soaked in kirsch liqueur—was out of this world.

By now the tension of the last few weeks, the trauma of her dash to France, her lack of sleep the night before and the presence of Jacques still so firmly in her life had reduced Sandi to a mindless robot that walked and talked and obeyed almost without question. She was utterly exhausted, mentally and physically and emotionally, and Jacques knew it, glancing at her anxiously once or twice when they were back in the car after their meal.

'Here.' He drew into a small lay-by on a winding road that overlooked a massive monastery, which was sleeping in the blazing hot sun and surrounded by orchards and sweet-smelling meadows. He adjusted her seat into a reclining position. 'Go to sleep. It will take us some time to get to Savoie—we have to go through Burgundy first, and then Rhône—and you look awful.'

'Huh...' It was all she could manage, and within seconds of lying back and shutting her eyes she was sound asleep, her hair falling in riotous abandon about her face and throat and deep mauve shadows staining the honey-coloured skin under her eyes.

When she next opened her eyes, dazed and light-headed from the hours of much needed sleep, it was evening and they were approaching the region of Savoie. The evening was mellow with dusky golden sunshine, fresh pure air streaming into the car through the open windows and the banks at the side of the road and the meadows beyond alive with brilliant wild flowers. 'I—I must have fallen asleep,' she murmured as she struggled to come fully awake.

'Like the proverbial log—except logs don't snore.' Jacques glanced at her with a wry smile and his words brought her jolting upright.

'I do not *snore*,' she stated emphatically, hearing his dry chuckle with a feeling of helpless panic. This was too cosy, too... nice... The word Jacques objected to so much mocked her, but it was true, she thought pain-

fully. It was all too, too nice and he mustn't think—
'You can't keep me in this log cabin for ever, Jacques,
and you must know there is no chance of anything permanent between us,' she said quickly.

'Must I?' He didn't seem in the least perturbed as he
glanced at her briefly through narrowed black eyes.

'I mean it,' she stated flatly. 'This is all—all—'

'Ridiculous?' he put in helpfully. 'That is the word
you would normally choose, is it not?'

'It *is* ridiculous,' she said tightly. 'All this is ridiculous. We are ridiculous—'

'No.' Now the car swerved off the road and came to
a halt overlooking a picture-postcard village behind
which snow-capped mountains rose majestically into the
vivid blue sky. 'Not us. The situation may be—but that
is your fault, not mine.'

His voice was angry and throbbing with something
she didn't dare question, and for the first time that day
she realised that the control she had thought so steel-
like was only skin-deep.

'You are going to stay at the cabin with me, Sandi,
and you are going to talk to me, dammit. I am not going
to make love to you. Pleasurable though that would be
for both of us, it would confuse the issue right now—
and we have the rest of our lives to enjoy each other's
bodies.'

'Jacques—'

'And so we are going to talk—really talk. You are
going to open up that little Pandora's box and tell me
all about your fears, your anguish, your feelings of humiliation and pain, the grief... I want all of it—all of
it right out in the open where I can see it and deal with
it, and you will be healed. I am not Ian, Sandi—I think
you could probably travel the whole of the world before
you found a skunk like that again—but I am not a mind-
reader either, and I can't help you until you communicate with me.'

'I don't want help.' Her eyes were blinded by tears.

'Well, I do.' His voice was gruff and husky. 'Because I can't face the thought of letting you go now I've found you. It might be hell with you, if we don't get this thing sorted, but it would be utter torment without you. I love you, Sandi; I need you. The least you can do for me, if you love me as you say you do, is talk to me.'

'And if that doesn't change anything?' she asked brokenly. 'If I still don't feel I can trust you, marry you? What then?'

'You will.' He looked at her with a wealth of love in his eyes, his dark, handsome face serious and intent. 'I can't believe we have found each other against all the odds only to have it fall apart before it's even begun. I won't believe that.'

'Jacques—'

'No more words, not for now. We will find the cabin, we will have supper and we will sleep. Tomorrow is a new day.'

And the next day, when she awoke in the beautiful red-roofed *gîte* and walked out onto the wooden balcony that overlooked the crystal-clear waters of the shimmering lake just yards away, with nothing but distant cowbells to disturb the peace of the timeless Alpine valley, she remembered his words. Tomorrow was here—now. The thing was, was she brave enough for the soul-searching Jacques had spoken of?

And so a bitter-sweet, disturbing, painful and magical time began. A time of long walks hand in hand through Alpine meadows covered with carpet upon carpet of wild flowers, of swimming in their own secluded lake through long, hot summer days, of horse-riding along narrow mountain paths on mounts borrowed from the small riding school-cum-farm on the outskirts of the tiny village from where they fetched their food, and of evenings spent on the veranda of the cabin with the air gradually cooling as dusk filtered into the scorching blue sky.

And through it all Jacques was true to his word.
Beyond holding her hand and brief, controlled kisses
there was no lovemaking, although Sandi invited it time
and time again as her love for this proud, strong man
who had turned her world upside down grew deeper and
deeper. And slowly, very slowly, she found herself beginning to talk of everything that held her bound.

It was traumatic, frequently harrowing for both of
them, and there were times when Sandi raged and
shouted at him for putting her through it, but . . . it was
helping. More than she would ever have dreamt possible.

And still Jacques kept his distance. She had long ago
ceased to worry about her work—what Ann had told
them she had no idea, but that all seemed in another
world, another universe. But still, *still* she couldn't say
the words Jacques wanted to hear from her heart. Something was holding her back, keeping her from taking that
last step of faith, and as they neared the end of the first
week she felt she never would.

'Enjoying it?' Jacques's voice was lazy as he glanced
at her through narrowed black eyes.

'Uh-huh.' She smiled back as her hair blew in a golden
cloud about her tanned face. They had decided to try
and find a particularly enchanting valley that Jacques
remembered, accessible only on horseback, and now, as
the horses picked their way carefully along the wide
mountain path with steep gullys on both sides, she wondered how long this could go on. Because she couldn't
change; she knew that now. She could never marry again;
it was too big a step of trust—even with Jacques.

And then it happened. One moment they were drinking
in the pure, clean air laden with a thousand summer
scents, the sky a vivid deep blue above them and the
horses lazy and contented, and the next a small, twisting
snake slithered across the path in front of them, sending
both horses demented. Sandi felt herself begin to slip as
her horse reared up with a frantic neigh, made one desperate clutch at its mane, and then she had gone, falling

onto the path for one brief second before the force of her fall took her over the edge of the gully towards the ravine a hundred feet below.

Somehow her hands clutched at a small prickly bush a few feet down from the edge of the path as she fell, and although she felt the sharp thorns tear into her flesh she hung on with all her might as she screamed Jacques's name.

'*Sandi?*' He was peering over the edge in the next moment, and she saw him shut his eyes for an infinitesimal second at the sight of her clinging to the bush which was the only vegetation for miles on the hard granite rock where nothing survived the heat of the day. 'Thank God. Keep still. I'm coming.'

'You can't come down here—you'll fall; you'll be killed,' she sobbed in terror.

'I'm coming down. Just wait a moment.' His head disappeared, and within seconds loose pebbles and dust were falling in her face as he began to descend towards her inch by precarious inch, using the few small footholds and slight indentations in the rock-face as he came.

'Go back, Jacques; please go back. We'll both be killed. You can go and get help—'

'You won't hold on much longer.' She knew that, but the thought of him dying too was unbearable. 'Now, keep calm and do exactly as I say,' he said, with a control that was formidable.

'Jacques, the bush is beginning to loosen.' She screamed in terror as it gave a little, but in the next moment he had grabbed her wrist, his flesh hard and firm on hers.

'Let go. Let go of the bush now, Sandi, and I will get you up.'

'I can't.' She was crying, almost hysterical with fear, and the pain in her lacerated hands and the thought of trying to climb up the sheer rock-face with only a few niches in which to put her feet and bleeding hands were too much for her.

'Give me your other hand,' he said calmly, his voice strong and cool. 'Reach out to me, Sandi.'

'I can't—I can't let go...' The bush shuddered and moved again as she clung on, Jacques's hand holding her other wrist in a grip of iron.

'If you don't let go it will take you with it. Let go, Sandi.'

'*I can't—I can't!*' She had never known that fear such as she was feeling now could exist. It was numbing her mind, her body, sending her mindless.

'Then we'll both go together.' The shock of his words brought her out of the hysteria, and as she raised her head to look up at him she saw that he meant it.

'Let go of me. Save yourself,' she said faintly. 'It's pointless us both dying.'

'I can't live without you, Sandi.' He spoke without any emotion, in contrast to her breathless sobbing. 'I love you and you love me. In life, in death, I want to be with you. I can get us both out of this if you trust me, Sandi. Do you? Do you trust me?'

His face was blurred through the tears streaming down her face from a combination of pain, panic and shock, but as she felt him gripping her wrist with steel fingers she knew this was real. This was the end, the ultimate, the final challenge, and now it was here she wondered how she could have hesitated for so long.

'Yes...' Her voice was a soft whisper through her tears, and then she drew in a deep breath as she reached out with her other hand, knowing they were both dependent now on the kindness of God and the mountain. 'Yes, I do trust you, Jacques. I trust you absolutely.'

By the time they had inched their way to the path, slowly and painfully, they were both drenched with their own sweat and smeared with grey dust and blood from her bleeding hands. They lay for long minutes in each other's arms without moving or speaking, their hearts pounding like sledgehammers and their limbs like lead. And then a bronzed, dirty hand turned her face towards his and she saw that he was smiling, his eyes warm as they devoured her tear-stained face.

'I told Ann I was going to make you trust me whatever it took,' he murmured softly. 'Can you remind me to watch what I say in the future?'

'Oh, Jacques, I love you. I love you so much,' she said shakily.

'And trust me?' he asked softly.

'And trust you,' she promised huskily.

'Then you may kiss me.' He pulled her on top of him, holding her very tightly, and as her mouth sought his the kiss deepened and held. 'And you will marry me?' he asked against her lips. 'Straight away?'

'Tomorrow, if you want,' she agreed breathlessly.

'I don't know if I can wait that long,' he said gruffly, his voice filled with a fierce exultation that stirred her heart. 'Oh, my love, my love. I'm going to make it all up to you. You're going to be loved like no woman has ever been loved before, do you know that?'

'Yes...' She was laughing now, her heart and mind free at last from the shackles of bitterness and pain. And then, as he groaned his need of her against her lips, his mouth taking hers with a fierce passion, there was only the blue sky above and the soaring mountains beyond, and two hearts entwined and ready to continue down the road of life, together at last for eternity.

MILLS & BOON®

Next Month's Romances

♡

Each month you can choose from a wide variety of romance with Mills & Boon. Below are the new titles to look out for next month in our two new series Presents and Enchanted.

Presents™

ONE-MAN WOMAN	Carole Mortimer
MEANT TO MARRY	Robyn Donald
AUNT LUCY'S LOVER	Miranda Lee
HIS SLEEPING PARTNER	Elizabeth Oldfield
DOMINIC'S CHILD	Catherine Spencer
JILTED BRIDE	Elizabeth Power
LIVING WITH THE ENEMY	Laura Martin
THE TROPHY WIFE	Rosalie Ash

Enchanted™

NO MORE SECRETS	Catherine George
DADDY'S LITTLE HELPER	Debbie Macomber
ONCE BURNED	Margaret Way
REBEL IN DISGUISE	Lucy Gordon
FIRST-TIME FATHER	Emma Richmond
HONEYMOON ASSIGNMENT	Sally Carr
WHERE THERE'S A WILL	Day Leclaire
DESERT WEDDING	Alexandra Scott

Return this coupon and we'll send you 4 Mills & Boon Presents™ novels and a mystery gift absolutely FREE! We'll even pay the postage and packing for you.

We're making you this offer to introduce you to the benefits of Reader Service: FREE home delivery of brand-new Mills & Boon Presents novels, at least a month before they are available in the shops, FREE gifts and a monthly Newsletter packed with information.

Accepting these FREE books and gift places you under no obligation to buy, you may cancel at any time, even after receiving just your free shipment. Simply complete the coupon below and send it to:

MILLS & BOON® READER SERVICE, FREEPOST, CROYDON, SURREY, CR9 3WZ.

No stamp needed

Yes, please send me 4 free Mills & Boon Presents novels and a mystery gift. I understand that unless you hear from me, I will receive 6 superb new titles every month for just £2.10* each postage and packing free. I am under no obligation to purchase any books and I may cancel or suspend my subscription at any time, but the free books and gifts will be mine to keep in any case. (I am over 18 years of age)

P6JE

Ms/Mrs/Miss/Mr _____

Address _____

_____

_____ Postcode_____

Offer closes 30th April 1997. We reserve the right to refuse an application. *Prices and terms subject to change without notice. Offer only valid in UK and Ireland and is not available to current subscribers to this series. **Readers in Ireland please write to: P.O. Box 4546, Dublin 24.** Overseas readers please write for details.

You may be mailed with offers from other reputable companies as a result of this application. Please tick box if you would prefer not to receive such offers. ☐

MILLS & BOON®

Celebrate the magic of Christmas!

With the Mills & Boon Christmas Gift Pack...

Mistletoe Magic

We've brought together four delightful romances from our
bestselling authors especially for you
this Christmas!

Her Christmas Fantasy
by **Penny Jordan**

Christmas Nights
by **Sally Wentworth**

A Mistletoe Marriage
by **Jeanne Allan**

Kissing Santa
by **Jessica Hart**

Special
Christmas
Price
£6.30